Learning to Think ...

Leadership

Understanding
Dr. Mikel J. Harry's
Six Sigma Way of Thinking

Alan M. Leduc

MW00637043

This publication is designed to provide accurate and authoritative information regarding the subject matter covered. It is sold with the understanding that the publisher and author are not engaged in rendering legal, accounting, or other professional services. If legal advice or other expert assistance is required, the services of a competent professional should be sought.

Copyright ©2019 Alan M. Leduc

All rights reserved. No part of this publication may be reproduced, distributed, or transmitted in any form or by any means, including photocopying, recording, or other electronic or mechanical methods, without the prior written permission of the publisher, except in the case of brief quotations embodied in critical reviews and certain other noncommercial uses permitted by copyright law. For permission requests, write to the publisher, addressed "Attention: Permissions Coordinator," at the address below.

BOPI Solutions LLC
251 Midway Drive
New Castle, IN 47362

Six Sigma ® is a registered trademark of Motorola, Inc.
The Great Discovery ® is a registered trademark of Dr. Mikel J. Harry, Ltd.
The Six Sigma Way of Thinking ® is a registered trademark of Dr. Mikel J. Harry, Ltd.
ICRA ® is a registered trademark of Dr. Mikel J. Harry, Ltd.
Executive Master Black Belt ® is a registered trademark of Dr. Mikel J. Harry, Ltd.
A Process that Creates Breakthrough in Everything You Do ® is a registered trademark of
       Dr. Mikel J. Harry, Ltd.
Learning to Think ® is a registered trademark of BOPI Solutions, LLC.

ISBN Hardback: 978-0-9847922-4-5
ISBN Paperback: 978-0-9847922-3-8
ISBN Ebook: 978-0-9847922-5-2

Library of Congress Control Number: 2019917852

Learning to Think… Leadership: Understanding Dr. Mikel J. Harry's Six Sigma Way of Thinking

First Edition

Credit: Editor: Barbara Smith
               Front Cover: Barbara Smith
               Index: Meredith Murray

Acknowledgements

To my teacher, my friend, my mentor, and my research partner Dr. Mikel J. Harry, who passed in 2017. I wish you were here to work with me on this project. I miss our long conversations, both personal and professional. During this work we had several conversations, although you were not physically present. Your philosophy and ideas are embedded in my mind.

To my wife, Brenda, who spent hours proofing my work and tolerating my singular focus, your contributions are immeasurable.

To my sister, Cindy Leduc, who is a retired fourth grade teacher. Thank you very much for proof reading and editing. You proved not all engineers know grammar as well as a fourth grader, or at least an excellent fourth grade teacher.

To my friend and editor, Barbara Smith. Thank you for your diligence and patience, guiding me through this project. Your knowledge and skills humble me. You both challenged me and forced me to think deeper. It was your motivation and knowing that you would be there to help me, that kept me pushing forward. It is a pleasure to work with you. You were more like a partner than an editor.

To Don Linsenmann and Phong Vu, thank you for agreeing to review this book and to contribute to the section on The Legacy of Dr. Mikel J. Harry.

To my friends and fellow Executive Master Black Belts, Sandra Harry, Cathy Lawson, and Jeff Heslop, thank you for your review of my thought process as I conveyed these concepts for the first time and for your contributions to the section on The Legacy of Dr. Mikel J. Harry.

I have had great life teachers, most of whom have now passed: Jack Renner, Gale Tarr, Robert Crooks, Wesley Baldwin, and Mikel Harry. Thank you for believing in me and making me better. Your combined contributions to my life are a significant part of who I am today.

Table of Contents

List of Figures

The Legacy of
Dr. Mikel J. Harry

December 28, 1951 – April 25, 2017

I would encourage you to read these personal comments by some of those who knew Mikel the best. And then when you have completed the book, come back and read them again.

Everyday is a holiday and every meal is a banquet - Every man and woman like a king and queen - In the land of milk and honey - Where the sun never sets and the moon always shines - it's just another opportunity to discover new ways to better serve my fellow man and make tomorrow's day even better.

Comments by Sandra Harry
Six Sigma Management Institute Chairman of the Board
Executive Master Black Belt

I met Mikel in May of 2008 and we were married on November 7, 2009. I held him as he left us early the morning of April 25, 2017. It was the most difficult but most beautiful thing I have every done in my life. He was my husband, friend, co-worker and mentor. One of our favorite things was discussion of just about any topic and telling stories. Mikel had so many fascinating stories I could write an entire book on just his stories. We would have long conversations and the more I listened to him the more I understood how special his thought process was. It was like none I had ever encountered before.

At the time I met Mikel I worked in corporate America. My focus was accounting and finance. I had recently completed an Executive MBA (EMBA). I was not a certified Lean Six Sigma Black Belt but had studied Six Sigma at a high level in my EMBA. The company I worked for had just starting on its journey of "Operational Excellence/World Class Performance". Unfortunately, the company was sold, and I left for a consulting position.

Looking back now, I feel fortunate that I was not a certified Black Belt when I met Mikel. Mikel had been working on The Great Discovery (TGD), the fourth generation of Six Sigma, for a couple years before I met him. He taught me TGD on backs of napkins when we would be out to dinner. He walked me through the Proven Path (underlying cognitive roadmap of TGD) as we walked through life each day. This way of thinking, the Six Sigma Way of Thinking, came very natural for me. I saw the power of TGD immediately and fell in love with it. At this point, my view of the world had completely changed. I now used the Six Sigma Way of Thinking in all aspects of my life.

I went on to get my Black Belt, Master Black Belt and Executive Master Black Belt certifications, but having TGD as my foundation was a huge advantage. The Great Discovery had taught me the Six Sigma Way of Thinking before adding all the statistics of belt training. Mikel often said, "I should have created TGD first then Six Sigma." I feel so honored to have been mentored by Mikel as he was polishing TGD.

When I agreed to work for Mikel at the Dr. Mikel J. Harry Six Sigma Management Institute, I had no idea of the impact it would have on me. Mikel's thought processes coupled with his "deep thinking" amazed me. But it was very difficult for me to shift into this environment. In corporate America, we are taught to make decisions fast, there is really no time for "deep thinking." Looking back at my time in leadership in corporate America, we were working on what I now know as the Y side of the equation. We were just throwing out potential solutions and hoping one would stick. Mikel taught me to work on the X side of the equation, the causative side, and to slow down and use "deep thinking". It has been a second order change for me, I can never go back to the old way.

I sat through all the Executive Master Black Belt classes. You would think that after the first one or two classes I would have been bored... not with Mikel teaching. He had a special way of teaching, even if you knew the information you would still learn more and understand the rest at a higher level. He was a master in front of a classroom. I loved every class. During those classes, Mikel spoke about many aspects of leadership. A few I will never forget are "managers follow policies and procedures... leaders have to improvise and adapt in the light of ambiguity", "if you don't hear the sound of flak flying around you... you are not leading" and "the eradication of fear." In all my years of education I had never heard anything like these concepts. They are part of my thought process now and I will always use them. Mikel was truly not only a leader but a thought leader.

Mikel taught me so much, but The Great Discovery, the Mikel J. Harry Way of Thinking, was the most profound. At the heart of TGD is coming to understand and living out our intrinsic core values. As a leader you cannot just make up a list of values and expect that everyone in the company shares those values. Each person has their own intrinsic core values and our job as leaders is to ensure everyone is living out those core values on a daily basis. Once this is achieved, then we can set the values of a work team, department or corporation and work together to achieve those. People are much more willing to participate when they know their values will be achieved and they can help others achieve their values as well. We can do this in our personal lives also. This is true leadership whether it be in a corporation, your personal life, or your home life.

Mikel once told me that it took about six months to create Six Sigma but his work on TGD spanned across many years. His tenacity to get TGD to a process that everyone could use was none like I had seen before. When Mikel went into work mode he would work for days and weeks on end. Many times, I would find him asleep at his computer. At this point, I honestly think Mikel was burned out on Six Sigma and his true passion was TGD and making sure everyone (the other 95%) could use it. His vision was to make the world a better place.

As Alan wrote this book, he would ask me to look through Mikel's work for information that would assist him. We would also have conversations about Mikel's work and the history. As the book unfolded, it hit me as to the magnitude of Mikel's thought process and as a thought leader. Mikel use to tell me that when he was young, he decided he wanted to create the world's best problem-solving system. For his doctoral program he wrote his own curriculum as no school in the US had a curriculum that would support his goal. Mikel's thought process was well underway by this time. During his doctoral program he created the Logic Filters. Most people do not know this, but Motorola GEG formally adopted Mikel's logic filters is 1984. An entire year before Bill Smith coined the term Six Sigma. Mikel's way of thinking was already being used at Motorola and as Alan states, Six Sigma was his merely his catalyst.

When asked about being a thought leader, Mikel would say "no not me". Mikel was very humble, but the truth is very clearly shown in this book. He was a great thought leader and I have to thank Alan for putting it in writing for all the world to see.

In the absence of fact, faith is the basis of belief

Comments by Don R. Linsenmann

CEO Executive Transformation Mentoring
Former DuPont Former Vice President and
Six Sigma Corporate Champion

The Business, Transformation, and Operational Excellence
Dr. Mikel J. Harry Six Sigma Lifetime Achievement Award
for Operational Excellence

"Mon Général, I think today you will need the red jacket AND the brown pants!" This is the punch line to one of Mikel's many stories that he used with management teams to motivate them to begin the journey to Six Sigma. He did not start with DPMO (Defects per Million Opportunities), Minitab (Statistical Software), or any statistical formula, but with a challenge to transform a Management team into a Leadership team. Vision, courage, conviction, culture, people - these were the dimensions of the transformation that Mikel knew would be the attributes of a successful journey to Six Sigma.

Former DuPont CEO, Chad Holliday, decided to launch Six Sigma at DuPont in the late nineties after doing some personal benchmarking with Jack Welsh and Larry Bossidy. He asked me to figure out how to deploy Six Sigma in all of DuPont's businesses, functions, and regions.

My first order of business was to fly to Scottsdale and meet Mikel. That started a relationship that evolved from working with a consultant, to learning from a teacher, to partnering on a corporate wide rollout, to collaborating on a book, to appreciating a mentor, and building a solid friendship.

My interactions with Mikel gave me the chance to transcend the day-to-day work of the Company and look at the possible transformation of a world class Company to one that uses the Six Sigma cultural attributes as the way the Company does business. Mikel always stressed how we could focus on the Quality of our Business, NOT the Business of Quality. This opened up a very powerful approach to transforming a culture, using the Big Ideas and expanding the proven results of Six Sigma to not only improve product quality and cost, but also to grow the enterprise through Top Line Growth and Innovation. This was a very creative time for those of us on the Journey.

One aspect of Mikel's thought process was the power of Leverage. This was a Big Idea. We discussed how I could have the most impact in leading the Six Sigma journey without the traditional organizational structure. The role of Champion fit this concept perfectly.

While being accountable for the enterprise metrics, results, progress, and strategy, the Corporate Champion did not need a formal organization. For maximum leverage, a network of business, functional, and regional champions reporting to their respective leaders was established. This network then delivered the billions of dollars of value throughout the Company. Other nested networks were created to leverage the knowledge in many areas, such as finance, IT, top line growth, and many more.

As this book points out, Mikel was a thought leader and was always looking to expand the base of thought to be relevant to ever growing audiences. This is best demonstrated as he defined the multi-generational evolution of Six Sigma.

I had the honor of receiving the Mikel J Harry lifetime achievement award in 2018 and I left the audience with a mnemonic for them to remember critical thoughts that reminded me of Mikel.

M... be a Mentor

I... be an Innovator

K... be an intellectually curious Kid

E... be an Educator

L... be a Leader

M – I – K – E -L

A view of the truth can be obtained by assembly of the facts.

Comments by Phong Vu

Former CEO, Six Sigma Management Institute
Former Ford Motor Company Director, Corporate Quality and Six Sigma Deployment

I was the Chief Engineer for the Ford F250 Super Duty truck. Even before its launch we knew it was going to be highly successful. Its pending release had gotten a lot of exposure and terrific reviews. I was very proud, and my accomplishments were recognized by the Company. I was promoted to Director of Quality and found myself in a very unusual position. I had been responsible for getting the F250 through design and production and now I was responsible for dealing with any issues that arose with my "baby" as it was delivered into the hands of our customers.

No product is perfect and as problems began to be exposed, I became ashamed of my work as Chief Engineer. I had followed Ford's quality guidelines explicitly and passed every test with flying colors. In fact, in most cases, we had far exceeded design and quality guidelines. Why were we having these problems?

I went to my boss and told him that I had followed company policies meticulously and they did not seem to have worked. When checking on problems that were occurring with our customers, every design and manufacturing box seemed be checked but the problems still existed. I told him, "We need to change the way we are doing things." and he responded, "That is now your job. What are you going to do?"

I assigned all of my daily duties to my Deputy and took three months to investigate and ponder the issue. It was during this time, that I met Dr. Mikel J. Harry. I was aware of his accomplishments at General Electric with Six Sigma and wanted to pick his brain.

Mikel's major focus at General Electric had been on the bottom line. Making higher profits short-term was terrific, but I could eliminate 10,000 jobs by taking out my pen writing my signature. I was looking for more, this is when Mikel and I began a conversation about the importance of Customer Satisfaction. I later learned that our change of focus from the bottom line to customer satisfaction was the beginning of what Mikel would call Generation III Six Sigma. At Ford we had a motto: "It starts with the customer, ends with the money, by elimination of waste in the middle."

Mikel was a genius. Even when he talked to executives, he was so out in front of them they often couldn't keep up. If an executive would say something that was not in line with the thoughts Mikel was presenting, he would frequently become frustrated and sometimes would "poke them in the eye" with a belittling comment. These were smart people with big egos and getting poked in the eye was not effective. I liked to view myself as Mikel's translator. Sometimes, I would tell Mikel, "Why don't you sleep in this morning, I have some translation to do."

As Mikel's translator, I determined from the executives their top three problems and talked to them about their values. I would then ask how much each of these "big problems" were worth to them? How did their values impact these "big problems?" Most frequently, they did not know. This gave us a place to start and an opportunity to start treating the "poke in the eye" Mikel had given them. I was able to translate Mikel's passion into something they could get behind. We made a great team that led to deployments of Six Sigma at Ford, AT&T and many others.

I learned three major things from Mikel:

- Behavior is related to Values
- $Y = f(X)$, Determinism
- If you don't know you can't act. If you do know, failure to act is a dereliction of duty.

The latter was a very important hook for executives. Mikel would tell them that I have now explained to you what you didn't know and now you have not choice but to act.

Mikel and I were both Marines. In fact, we served at the same time and had the same instructors. This gave us a special bond. I left Ford to consult and Mikel and I teamed up through the Dr. Mikel J. Harry Six Sigma Management Institute where I became CEO. Mikel was tired of traveling and began working on MindPro, his online Six Sigma training. I believe Mikel worked harder on MindPro than he had worked at any of his major deployments. He was up early in the morning, working late into the night. I was out doing the consulting and deployments. When I encountered big problems, I would call Mikel and he would start off by telling me how busy he was, insinuating I just needed to handle it. This is when I reminded him, "Mikel, remember we are Marine buddies, you can't leave a buddy behind." The special bond never failed.

Mikel was not just my colleague but my friend. I was one of the few people Mikel allowed to challenge him. I think this is because I understood his way of thinking. I had come to realize much of what Six Sigma had become was teaching of tools. I realized that Six Sigma was really the thought process itself. Mikel taught me that that process and I have been able to translate it in my own way to the world.

> *To improve means we must be able to predict and prevent, not detect and react.*
>
>

S. Jeff Heslop

Former GE Aviation Master Black Belt
Executive Master Black Belt

I became aware of Mikel Harry in the 1990s while working for GE Aircraft Engines (now GE Aviation), as a Total Quality Advisor in Continuous Improvement, while attending a Design for Manufacturing course taught by Motorola. About this time, Jack Welch, CEO of General Electric, had learned of Six Sigma from Larry Bossidy, CEO of Allied Signal and decided to deploy Six Sigma throughout GE.

In the fall of 1995, because of my involvement in Continuous Improvement, I was chosen to be a part of the first GE Aircraft Engines Six Sigma Master Black Belt (MBB) class. The MBB candidates and GE executives from the various GE businesses all traveled to the Crotonville, New York training center to be taught by Dr. Mikel Harry for two weeks. We met in the "pit", a large amphitheater, where Mikel taught us.

Mikel was clearly in command and very confident as he thundered at us with Six Sigma principles and statistics. I remember that one of our seasoned professionals had challenged him a time or two. Mikel told him, "I have been doing this longer than you have been thinking about it!" That got quite a good rise from the packed house.

My initial impression of Mikel was that he was very sure of himself, but later learned from him that he was very nervous and stressed over how quickly Welch wanted to move forward with Six Sigma. Welch was pushing Mikel to deploy in a way that had never been done before. Mikel's approach had always been to train Black Belts first and then choose the best of them to move on to become Master Black Belts. But Welch wanted his Master Black Belts trained first and Mikel had no choice but to agree. For the first time, Mikel was training Master Black Belts who had not already been through Black Belt training. Mikel never gave us any hint of his nervousness, but in later years confessed how intimidating the "pit" had been.

Mikel was an excellent and very demanding trainer. Even from "the pit" with that large audience, he interacted with the students. There were so many questions, yet he patiently answered all of them. Mikel gave us homework each evening. Each GE business unit would then report out the next morning. We worked on these homework assignments late at night, even into the early morning hours. We were in competition with the other business units to have the best report out and to be judged by Mikel as being the "best."

Mikel had learned that a company must link their Six Sigma projects to time and money, the language of the C-suite (Chairman, Executive Suite). After the first class completed their projects, it was easy to see that Six Sigma was not only good for quality and the customer, but also for the financial bottom line of the company. This was an enormous distinction between Six Sigma and Continuous Improvement.

I remained in an MBB role until I retired in 2014. Then in 2015 I was invited to attend Mikel's Executive Master Black Belt (EMBB) class in Scottsdale, AZ. Mikel had decided to train a small cadre of EMBBs to carry on his legacy and to prevent the dilution of Six Sigma that had become so common among consultants. I had started my own Six Sigma consulting business by then. So the opportunity to learn from Mikel once again, particularly at this level, was one of the most exciting times of my career.

Mikel only allowed about four students at a time in a class so he could pour his knowledge into each candidate on a personal level. We listened to a few principles then talked them out together. He did very little lecturing. Although I had had many years of experience as an MBB at GE, I was humbled by how little I knew of Six Sigma Thinking. I had learned well what Mikel called Generation II Six Sigma, but Mikel was in Generation III and beyond. I learned while Generation II was about reducing cost, Generation III was about adding value for both the customer and provider. Mikel taught us not only the concepts, but how to accomplish them.

The stories Mikel told the class about his experiences in deploying Six Sigma with various companies were fascinating. We learned how tenacious he had to be with executives to bring about change. He shared his personal insights on the best practices for successful deployment of Six Sigma, how to speak the language of the C-suite, how to use Six Sigma tools in financial analysis, how to analyze data to find the critical areas with the highest leverage.

I set my expectations so high, anticipating the EMBB class. Little did I know that I didn't know enough to properly set expectations.

I realized that I and everybody else in the room had absorbed only a fraction of Mikel's knowledge. We left yearning for more. The class was like having a personal conversation with Mikel for a whole week. When Friday came, I was not ready to go home. Now that's saying something since I am a homebody. I even went back a second time to take the class again and still learned more. I have no doubt that had I attended over and over, I would still yearn for more. Mikel had so much knowledge to share.

Personally, I gained a friend. Professionally, Mikel gave me confidence to engage with executives and share with them the knowledge that Mikel shared with me. I am able to teach them a proven and repeatable roadmap for success. I believe Six Sigma thinking should be required training for every leader.

Mikel's legacy continues with his MindPro online training platform. MindPro contains hundreds of videos where you are looking over the shoulder of Mikel as he teaches and illustrates with his hand drawn sketches. Mikel doesn't focus just on how the tools work but shows you how to apply the tools. I have completed the Black Belt certification again using MindPro through Dr. Mikel J. Harry Six Sigma Management Institute, just to hear him teach these things in his own words and style. This is a great way for students to learn.

Some say that Six Sigma is nothing new, that it is just repackaged best practices from the past. There is a lot in common with previous best practices for sure, but I disagree that there is nothing new or innovative. While many of the tools are common, Dr. Mikel J. Harry's Six Sigma Way of Thinking is not common. Mikel's way of thinking is the real genius behind Six Sigma.

I had the opportunity to be a beta-reader for this book. As a Six Sigma Black Belt and Master Black, and having attended two Executive Master Black Belt classes, I had come to understand the importance of Mikel's thought systems from the Logic Filters, to MAIC, to DMAIC, and what Mikel called The Breakthrough Strategy. Alan Leduc reveals in this book Mikel's most mature thinking. Alan has researched and labored to dissect and expand Mikel's thought systems and link them into a complete integrated thought system. Every leader should learn Dr. Mikel J. Harry's complete thought system and teach it to others.

Mikel expressed that Value Creation and the rate it is created, what Mikel called Velocity of Value, is role of a Leader. Alan expresses that Learning to Think like a Leader is the pathway that Mikel provided to us for accomplishing this task. First, we must learn to think like a Leader. This will teach us how to create value. Then we must use our newly learned Leadership Thinking over and over until it becomes our nature. And we must share our new knowledge of

Leadership Thinking with others. These latter two actions create Velocity of Value.

As a person, Mikel is to be honored for unselfishly sharing with the world his way of thinking. I believe every MBA curriculum should include Mikel's Six Sigma thinking for leaders. Mikel should be honored for both his service to our country (as a Marine) and for his love for our veterans. He was a man of faith who gave to others because of the blessings he received from God. Mikel gave back to the world.

> *To change the answer is to change the question.*
>
>

Comments by Cathy Lawson

Former Medtronic Engineering Manager/ Master Black Belt
Former General Dynamics Quality Director
Former Motorola Six Sigma Black Belt
Executive Master Black Belt

I was hired at Motorola Government Electronics in August of 1985. Three weeks after I started, I was asked to attend an industrial statistics class that was taught by Dr. Mikel Harry. I loved everything about the class, especially the way he taught the material. That started a mentor/mentee relationship between Mikel and I that continued for over thirty years.

When Six Sigma was first proposed at Motorola, Mikel was tapped by CEO Bob Galvin to supply the framework and thought process for how it would be implemented. Mikel wrote the *Nature of Six Sigma Quality*[1] and began applying his logic filter framework to the implementation of Six Sigma. He assembled a team of people that he named the Statistics Advisory Council to serve as a steering committee for the application of statistics and process thinking to Six Sigma projects. I was really excited to be named to that Council. While all this was getting started, my father, James R. Lawson moved from the semiconductor part of Motorola to the Government Electronics Group and was assigned to work with Mikel. Now I had my father and Mikel as teachers and mentors as we explored this fascinating new world known as Six Sigma. What a fun time to be working as a young engineer in industry!

I could write volumes about my relationship with Mikel and the effect he had on my career and more importantly my thought process. But given this is Alan's book, I will confine my remaining comments to a few key topics that were the most impactful.

Being part of the Statistics Advisory Council, another key moment was the discussion that Mikel started where he talked about the germination of the idea of the Six Sigma Black Belt. His original idea was that a Black Belt was someone who first was recognized as a technical expert in his/her original area of study, i.e., electrical engineer, physicist, mathematician, etc. Second, a Black Belt was someone who could successfully apply the Six Sigma principles to achieve Breakthrough performance in a process or product. Third, a Black Belt had "soft" skills, i.e., interpersonal skills, that allowed him/her to serve as a change agent, influencer, leader and teacher to name a few roles. For me it was a privilege to be considered one of the first Six Sigma Black Belts, especially according to his definition.

Mikel eventually left Motorola to consult and spread the Six Sigma Way of Thinking. I kept in contact with him during those years but didn't get an opportunity to work with him again until 2009. At that point in time he invited me to attend a class he was going to hold to roll out what he was calling the fourth generation of Six Sigma, otherwise known as The Great Discovery. I was very excited about that because Mikel had indicated this was bringing Six Sigma to help people advance and achieve breakthrough in their personal lives. I completely resonated with that idea because I had implemented some of the key learnings from Six Sigma to my own personal life and I was excited to see how Mikel was formalizing that thought process. Then later that year he honored me again when he asked me to co-author a book about The Great Discovery.

From a professional standpoint, Mikel was my teacher and my mentor. I was one of the first certified Black Belts at Motorola and in the world. I became a Master Black Belt in 1998. I was invited by Mikel to attend The Great Discovery training and later became a The Great Discovery coach. In 2014, Mikel invited me to attend his first Executive Master Black Belt training and I achieved Certified EMBB #0002 a few months later.

From a personal standpoint Mikel was my friend. I went to many parties and dinners at his house and enjoyed many wonderful and sometimes challenging conversations with him. Through Mikel I met Alan Leduc whose friendship I also highly value. Additionally, I met Sandra Harry, my birthday buddy (we are born two days apart) and my dear friend, through Mikel. I am profoundly grateful for having the opportunity to have worked with Mikel, learn from Mikel, and enjoy friendship with Mikel for over thirty years.

Alan ask me to cite a specific incident or my way of Leadership that I could attribute to Mikel's thought processes. This is an easy one for me because it was such a profound realization when I had this conversation with Mikel. I believe this is the foundation for Alan's book—Learning to Think… Leadership. As Alan points out, Mikel had been concerned for some time about the level of adoption of the Six Sigma Way of Thinking among the belts and students that he had taught over the years. This concern was first voiced by Jack Welch, CEO of General Electric, when Mikel was asking him about the highs and lows of the Six Sigma implementation at GE. Jack Welch said that he wondered how they could give Six Sigma to "the other 95%". Mikel shared this comment with me at a later point in time when he was still thinking about it and wrestling with the idea. The concern that Jack Welch expressed—and that Mikel realized— was that only about 5% of the people who had been exposed to Six Sigma training and application really got it at a deep foundational level. When I heard Mikel express that I was quick to argue. "But Mikel, more than 5% of the people you have taught are Black Belts." I protested. "Surely at least Black Belts get Six Sigma." He corrected me. He told me that while people might be able to lead a project using the Six Sigma Breakthrough Strategy and tools and even go on to complete the Black Belt certification, that only about 5% of the population understood the Six Sigma Way of Thinking. He then went on to tell me that I wasn't quite comprehending this because I was one of the 5% and that was the way my thought process worked naturally.

That conversation gave me pause. I pondered it for a long time, and I tried to understand what he was saying. As I interacted with Six Sigma professionals, I began to realize what he was saying. There were those that naturally understood the ins and outs of Six Sigma, how to apply it, and how to achieve breakthrough results, but they were few and far between. This conversation gave me insights into how to discuss Six Sigma with current and future Belts. With a few simple questions I could determine fairly quickly if someone was in the 5% or not. If so, that meant I could have entirely different conversations with those people. I could push boundaries and explore new territory in ways that could not be done with people who did not practice the Six Sigma way of Thinking.

This is one of the reasons why I believe this book is so important. The Six Sigma Way of Thinking, Mikel Harry's Way of Thinking is really powerful. It allows a person or a team to achieve breakthrough performance in ways that cannot be imagined by those who do not think this way.

> *To know the truth is to know all of the facts. To know the facts requires investigation. Investigation is driven by questions.*

Comments by Alan M. Leduc
Author and Executive Master Black Belt #0001

Many know Dr. Mikel J. Harry as the co-creator and Chief Architect of Six Sigma. For me, Mikel was my teacher, my mentor, my friend, and my research partner. From that special relationship, I am in a unique position to share a deep understanding of not only Six Sigma and the Six Sigma Way of Thinking, but the personal philosophies and stories Mikel shared with me over those years.

I worked with Mikel as he developed the Executive Master Black Belt program (EMBB), and he honored me with EMBB #0001, of only 26 handpicked EMBB's worldwide, as a token of appreciation for my work. It was my honor to have worked with one of the world's great thought leaders, and I hope to do my part by extending Mikel's teachings to the next generation through the creation of this book.

My work with Mikel included updating and improving his MindPro Lean Six Sigma training which included the writing of a Simulated Case Study (Midco) that could be used for project assessment. My main role was to serve as one of Mikel's sounding boards as he developed The Great Discovery, which you will learn is the current personal model for what Mikel called his Breakthrough Strategy. And as mentioned above, I worked with Mikel on the Executive Master Black Belt Program. Over our tenure of working together, I was able to obtain on a personal one-to-one level: history, current thinking, and future thinking, some of which Mikel may not have shared with anyone else. We were able to relate on a personal level and a professional level. He allowed me to work with him, because he knew I would challenge him when I thought he was wrong, and I would inspire him by providing viewpoints that he may not have otherwise considered.

One of the things Mikel shared with me was that despite his notoriety revolving about Six Sigma, it was his desire to be remembered as a "Thought Leader." Mikel's thinking was profound and intense. I don't think his mind ever shut off. He seemed to be continually probing to improve his historical thought processes and innovate new ones; or to innovate new uses of old thought processes.

I viewed Mikel as the great "Thought Leader" he was. In the latter years, I repeatedly told Mikel that his "thought processes," starting with his doctoral work, were far more important than his revolutionary accomplishments with Six Sigma. While Mikel wanted to be known as a Thought Leader, he couldn't imagine anything being more important than the revolution he brought to the business world with Six Sigma. So our work continued to focus on exploring new uses of Six Sigma, many of which are likely to remain unpublished.

After Mikel's passing, I made a personal but unspoken commitment to do what I could to extend Mikel's legacy. I could not get out of my head how I had linked together Mikel's thought processes and came to understand them in such a way that they could be expressed as a form of Leadership. Mikel had refused to go down this road with me, but I knew that if I could pull his thought processes together in a systematic way, he would be proud of the result.

Mikel and I connected on a personal level as well as a professional level. Mikel and I were one year apart in age, Mikel being a year younger. I was fascinated by Mikel's hobbies as a "cowboy," race enthusiast, and musician. He was fascinated with my hobby as a long-distance motorcycle rider. If you look at the cover of many of Mikel's books, he is dressed in cowboy attire. He once told me a story of a CEO from a fortune 50 company wanting to meet with him, but the meeting conflicted with a rodeo. Mikel said, "Business is important, but nothing is more important than roping. I missed that meeting." We both had a passion for business but that wasn't unusual; we both had a passion for everything we did in life.

Oddly, our paths could have crossed many years before we finally met. Mikel and I grew up in small towns in Indiana that were only 16 miles apart. Both Mikel and I have degrees from Ball State University.

When Mikel and I worked in person, I stayed at his home. Mikel's wife Sandra made special blankets to give to her closest friends. Mikel's blanket was special in that it was made into a poncho. My fondest memory is Mikel setting on the back porch early in the morning elbows on thighs with head bowed. He wasn't sleeping. He was thinking, deep thinking.

It is hard to put Mikel's impact on my life into words. So I'm going to include some comments left on his memorial page,[2] as they express my feeling better than I can express myself.

People come into your life, for reasons... seasons... and lifetimes. I did not get to experience nearly as much time with him as I would have liked... and now it will be in the ethers. Mikel is, and always will be... a highly intuitive man. Someone who shares truth from his heart & always supports his friends in the quest of their greatest good. I loved our talks, we had so much fun sharing ideas... and it was always very exciting to be in that creative vortex with him... I always came away with priceless nuggets of possibilities! *Ellen Saravis*

As a true authentic developer of learning, one must feed the curiosity, as that is the driver for learning. Mikel did this on his death bed. What dedication, what passion, what selflessness. *Geoff Sander*

I still miss Dr. Mikel. He had a way of challenging my thinking. The world will never know what brilliant gifts he was preparing to give us next. *Steve Gottry*

It has been 17 months since my last conversation with Mike. When I think about that conversation it amazes me that it stays as strong a memory as it was the day after we spoke. That was the Mikel Effect. He always left a lasting impression. When my wife and I met she told me "You lead a blessed life." I had never thought about it like that. It was just life. She was right. What I have been allowed to experience isn't offered to many. That door to that life was opened by Mike as he drove his vision. I had a seat on a fast-moving train. *Mike Carnell*

Mikel was a giant among men. His shadow is large and it is inspirational to those of us that met and were trained by him. *Aubrey Jones*

He was one of the most articulate and charismatic business people I have ever met. He could, if required, summon advanced mathematical and engineering concepts from his vast memory, but he was equally adept at converting the most complex things into simple but powerful concepts, phrases, and images. *Bruce Miyashita*

Mikel, was a remarkable man. A Visionary, gifted in the ability to make the complex reachable, a man of strong convictions, and a very generous man. He made differences large and small. *Paul Borawski*

Mike had the admirable ability to express complex ideas simply and clearly. It enabled him to function effectively on the shop floor and in the C-suite. He genuinely liked people, and his passion was unmistakable. *Jonathan Andell*

ONE THING was the most evident in Mike at all times—his PASSION. Everything he did, he did with 1000 percent passion and total belief. *Richard Schroeder*

Mikel lit a flame that will forever burn! I loved how he treated everyone with compassion, respect, and left them with empowerment. *Jason Bickford*

Mikel taught me that life has order and answers are within our grasp. *Tim Fowler*

Mikel had a huge impact on my life. How many people get to work with "the person" in their field. Of course, I always viewed my sharing of knowledge as a one-way path from Mikel to me. Imagine the shock the first time Mikel told me how much I challenged him to think deeper. Imagine how I felt when Mikel told me, "I knew if you were questioning what I said, there had to be something wrong with my thinking." Imagine how scared and intimidated I was when Mikel first gave me an assignment to prepare on his behalf.

This book is dedicated to the legacy of my friend. In addition to the years I spent working with Mikel, I have spent hundreds of hours researching and pondering Mikel's thought system for this book. The result is that Mikel's thought systems have been intertwined into a complete thought system that will teach you that *Learning to Think… Leadership* is possible for **Anyone**. I'm confident that Mikel would have been proud about the way I have been able to develop his thought systems into a complete package. My only wish is that he had been here personally so that we could have developed this work as partners like we have done with so many other things.

The book is broken into Four Sections:

- The Legacy of Dr. Mikel J. Harry

- The Breakthrough Strategy; The Six Sigma Way of Thinking; Leadership

- Big Ideas

- ICRAtic Value Creation Strategy and Integration of Big Ideas

The first section, "The Legacy of Dr. Mikel J. Harry," includes this chapter and similar observations from others who had the opportunity to work with Mikel closely over the years. This is an opportunity for you to see Mikel as those close

to him did. I asked them to provide these comments to share their personal experiences, the impact Mikel had on their lives, and Mikel's contribution as a Thought Leader.

The second section of the book, "The Breakthrough Strategy; The Six Sigma Way of Thinking; Leadership" looks at the roots of The Breakthrough Strategy which Mikel called The Six Sigma Way of Thinking through to the current personal and commercial models for The Breakthrough Strategy. The section then concludes by showing how The Breakthrough Strategy – The Six Sigma Way of Thinking is synonymous with how Leaders think and is compatible with Leadership. Mikel's Breakthrough Strategy provides a means for teaching **Anybody** how to think like a leader. Understanding and beginning to utilize The Breakthrough Strategy is the first level of knowledge in Leadership Thinking.

The third section of the book discusses sixteen Big Ideas rooted in Mikel's Ten Supreme Laws and his ICRAtic Value Creation Strategy. While The Breakthrough Strategy is prescriptive, like a recipe for how to think like a Leader, the Big Ideas are more abstract, more conceptual. The Big Ideas are a checklist of concepts that must be gone through in our subconscious mind for every thought. These are concepts and principles that must become second nature to us.

The last section of the book discusses the highest level of Leadership Thinking focusing on Innovative Thinking as described by Mikel's ICRAtic Value Creation Strategy and then looking at how the Big Ideas are integrated into both ICRA and The Breakthrough Strategy. It shows how these Big Ideas can be combined to form an almost infinite number of permutations to advance thought.

The Breakthrough Strategy

The Six Sigma Way of Thinking

> *Facts are the notes of a song, the elements of an equation, and the form in sculpture.*
>
> ⎯⎯⎲⎳

Chapter 1
Introduction

This section of the book is on The Breakthrough Strategy: The Six Sigma Way of Thinking. You will be taken on a journey to understanding The Six Sigma Way of Thinking, or more accurately Dr. Mikel J. Harry's Way of Thinking, and come to understand it is synonymous with Leadership, and ***Anybody*** can learn to think like a leader. You will be presented models from the beginning of Mikel's thinking about how to solve problems through his final models. These models will help you understand the roots of Mikel's thinking in a way that both experts and laypeople can appreciate. This book is intended for a universal audience who want to move their thinking from ordinary to extraordinary whether it be in a role within an organization or their personal life.

Do an internet search on "What is Leadership" and you will find a seemingly infinite number of explanations. I have read and considered many of them. Most of these explanations provide the desired characteristics or traits desired for a Leader. But characteristics and traits are more about nature and difficult to change or to create in a person. I would love to be 6 feet tall and an operatic voice, but neither of those is likely to happen.

While researching for this book, I came to realize that Leadership starts with Thinking and that Mikel's thought processes provided a pathway for teaching ***Anybody*** how to think like a Leader in a teachable, repeatable, proven way. My definition of Leadership:

> **Leadership is defined by the way you think and your ability to share the way you think with others so that they too can be leaders.**

While this book will cover Six Sigma from a macro perspective, the book is not about Six Sigma; it's about what Dr. Mikel J. Harry considered the "Six Sigma Way of Thinking." By the time you are finished with the book, you should understand that referring to Mikel's way of Thinking as The Six Sigma Way of Thinking puts Mikel's thought process in a very narrow silo.

Although our focus is not on Six Sigma, I know many will have a hard time disassociating Mikel with Six Sigma. So, before going any further, I would like you to take some time and write down a summary of what you know about Six Sigma and what you think it is. This summary will serve as your baseline of knowledge. I am confident that by the end of the book, your perspective will be expanded well beyond your baseline.

What is Six Sigma? I have more than a million words in my research notes of Mikel's books, writings, and personal notes. Searching Mikel's work, I pulled up hundreds of references following the term, "Six Sigma is." Since Six Sigma has gone through four significant evolutions in its forty-year history, whatever you think you know about Six Sigma might be true, or it might have been true once but is no longer current. More than likely, even if you hold a Six Sigma Belt, you do not have a full understanding of "What Six Sigma is."

Dr. Stanley A. Marash, in his book *Fusion Management*,[3] notes he had been exposed to more than thirty (30) quality programs since 1960, most of which have come and gone. Marash made an important observation of not just why these quality programs failed but why many business initiatives fail. He notes:

> A common pattern emerges. A few pioneer companies adopt and develop a program and achieve great initial success. The business press takes notice, and other companies seek to emulate the pioneers. But as the idea spreads, it becomes diluted. Senior management tries to adopt the model without really ever comprehending what is required to make the program successful. These followers want the results but are unwilling to put in the same effort as the pioneers. They fail to measure their results, and they lack clear, focused goals.

Most of what we read regarding Six Sigma is based upon the deployment of Six Sigma at General Electric in the 1990s using the DMAIC (Define, Measure, Analyze, Improve, Control) thought process. Jack Welch is one of the most noted CEO's of our time, and his adoption and endorsement of Six Sigma was profound and highly documented by the business community.

While most Six Sigma experts know Six Sigma was introduced at Motorola in the 1980s, few know the thought process was MAIC (Measure, Analyze, Improve, Control), not DMAIC. The Define phase was not added until nearly a decade later at General Electric. Few Six Sigma experts are aware that Six Sigma evolved again in the 2000s at DuPont, even though this deployment is documented in *The Six Sigma Fieldbook: How DuPont Successfully Implemented the Six Sigma Breakthrough Management Strategy*[4] which was written in 2006 by Mikel Harry, Ph.D. and Don R. Linsenmann. And yet even fewer Six Sigma experts are aware that the MAIC thought process at Motorola was based upon

Mikel J. Harry's doctoral work called The Logic Filters, or that Mikel developed a personal model of the Six Sigma thought process focused on Human Achievement in the late 2000s called The Great Discovery. It is difficult to answer the question, "What is Six Sigma?" because Six Sigma experts and the business community are broadly unaware of the evolution of Six Sigma and the related thought systems.

I am confident the baseline knowledge I asked you to write down will not match your perception of Six Sigma after you have read this book. Your knowledge is likely dated and limited in scope. While the foundation of Six Sigma did not change, The Six Sigma Way of Thinking, what Mikel called The Breakthrough Strategy, and the focus of Six Sigma has evolved over four generations to what Mikel believed was a foundational level of knowledge. This book will guide you through the evolution of Six Sigma and guide you through the three levels of Leadership Thinking.

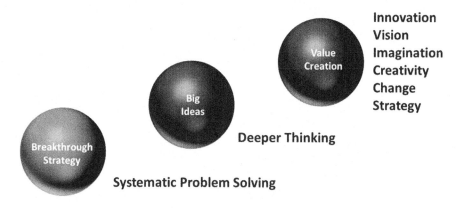

Figure 1 Three Levels of Leadership Thinking

Enjoy the journey, no matter whether you already believe you are an accomplished leader and understand the way you think, or you are new to leadership and are anxious to learn about a proven path that other successful leaders have taken. Maybe you desire to teach others how to become a leader. Or it may be that you want to think like a leader in your personal life. You will be pleased to learn that Leadership Thinking: The Six Sigma Way of Thinking – The Breakthrough Strategy, is teachable, repeatable, and proven. If you have a willingness to adapt your way of thinking, your thinking will move from ordinary to extraordinary.

As you read along, check the baseline summary of knowledge you developed and reflect on how your perspective is changing.

The difference between a smashing success and a failure does not revolve around statistical tools, or software, or various methods. It revolves around the magic of changing people's hearts and leading the collective soul to the land of breakthrough in a highly visible and accountable way.

Chapter 2
What is Six Sigma?

Whenever I'm first introduced to Lean Six Sigma Belts or those who want to discuss Six Sigma, I always like to start with a leading question, "How do you view Six Sigma:As a Quality Program; a Cost Reduction Program, or how would you classify it?" By starting with this leading question, I can get a good idea as to the source of their training and the currency of their Six Sigma knowledge. If they are a Belt, an excellent follow up question is "Who certified you?" so their training can later be traced back to one of the first three generations of Six Sigma: Generation I at Motorola in the 1980s; Generation II at General Electric in the 1990s; Generation III at DuPont in the 2000s.

As a result of the evolution of Six Sigma, Belts were trained in different generations of Six Sigma. Similarly, those claiming knowledge of Six Sigma likely are not familiar with the evolution of Six Sigma, and thus their knowledge is biased based upon where they garnered their knowledge.

Each evolution of Six Sigma had a different focus. Generation I at Motorola was a Quality Program with a focus on the customer. Generation II at General Electric was a Cost Reduction Program focused on the provider. Generation III at DuPont focused on the exchange of value for both the customer and the provider and is represented as the intersection of customer values and provider values, as shown in Figure 2. Mikel noted this intersection represented the business relationship and called it Value Entitlement. Generation III Six Sigma is considered the current commercial model for Six Sigma and focuses on business, as opposed to Quality in Generation I and Cost Reduction in

Generation II. As Mikel liked to say, "Six Sigma evolved from the business of quality to the quality of business."

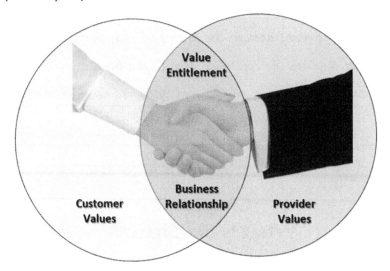

Value Entitlement

Customer Values

Business Relationship

Provider Values

Figure 2 Generation III - Value Entitlement

In addition to the three generations of commercial models, Mikel also developed a personal model of Six Sigma called The Great Discovery, which he considered the fourth Generation of Six Sigma. The focus of The Great Discovery is on human achievement, showing people from "the boardroom to the family kitchen table" how to move from ordinary thinking to extraordinary thinking. In an email to me, Mikel said, "In terms of The Great Discovery, I believe this is the best work I have ever accomplished (and perhaps the most powerful)." Keep in mind The Great Discovery followed many successful launches of Six Sigma with Fortune 50 companies. While Mikel felt that with Generation III of Six Sigma he had evolved Six Sigma to its core, he believed that with The Great Discovery he was able to communicate The Six Sigma Way of Thinking in a way *Anybody* could understand.

There are two current models for The Six Sigma Way of Thinking: Generation III and The Great Discovery. Generation III focuses on the quality of business (Value Entitlement) for the customer and provider, and The Great Discovery focuses on human achievement and presents The Six Sigma Way of Thinking in lay terms through a model *Anybody* can follow. Generation III was written for a commercial audience, while The Great Discovery was written for a personal audience.

Given this brief history on Six Sigma, it should be obvious that answering the question "What is Six Sigma?" will result in different responses depending on one's familiarity with the four generations of Six Sigma.

Before his passing, Mikel expressed to me that The Great Discovery would be the last evolution of Six Sigma. Mikel felt that after nearly 40 years, he had finally evolved Six Sigma to its core.

Six Sigma is rooted in three primary concepts

1. Variation Reduction
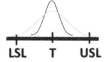

2. The Breakthrough Strategy DMAIC

3. Project-by-Project Implementation

Figure 3 Three Primary Concepts Underlying Six Sigma

To further complicate answering the question "What is Six Sigma?" we need to understand Six Sigma is often viewed from the perspective of the three primary concepts underlying Six Sigma: Variation Reduction, The Breakthrough Strategy, and Project-by-Project Implementation (Figure 3). These three primary concepts will be discussed individually in the next few chapters.

Chapter 3
Variation Reduction

The originating primary concept underlying Six Sigma was variation reduction with a focus on improving customer satisfaction through the reduction of defects. Bill Smith, the co-founder of Six Sigma with Mikel Harry, was focused on product design and reliability, known today as Design for Six Sigma. Smith came to realize that the key to better product reliability and better quality was through variation reduction (more consistency).

Traditionally, upper and lower specification limits were established, and the producer inspected and sorted products to meet those specifications, with no regard to variation. These sorting steps resulted in classifying product that falls between the specification limits as good, and classifying product that falls outside the specification limits as bad.

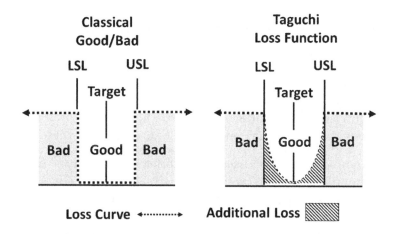

Figure 4 Impact of Taguchi's View of Variation

Genichi Taguchi developed his Quality Loss Function in the early 1970's, and it was popularized in the 1980s at about the same time as Smith's focus on variation. Taguchi's work changed the concept of how we look at conformance to specification. The Taguchi Loss Function stated that an increase in variation (even within specification limits) leads to an exponential increase in customer dissatisfaction, which results in additional loss between the specification limits. In other words, customers only feel an entitlement level of satisfaction at perfection and any variation away from the target will begin to incur customer dissatisfaction. (Figure 4). Douglas Montgomery, Regents Professor at Arizona State University and author of several statistics books, puts the importance of variation in perspective with his definition of quality. Montgomery says quite simply, "Quality is inversely proportional to variation."[5]

My fellow Executive Master Black Belt (EMBB) Cathy Lawson likes to use this example to explain Taguchi's thoughts regarding variation. When you go to buy shoes, you often find there is a significant variation in fit. Why? Well, because process variation may cause size 8 shoes to fit differently on your target size 8 foot. A small variation from your target foot may be acceptable. But as the size of the shoe deviates from your foot, either larger or smaller, your dissatisfaction becomes exponentially larger since the shoe does not fit properly or doesn't feel good. That's a loss to the customer. Or maybe the customer decides not to buy the shoe, and that's a loss to the provider.

With a classical design band of plus or minus three (3) sigma (plus or minus three (3) standard deviations of process performance), statistics tell us there should be 99.73% yield. Smith recognized this did not appear to be true as he was observing actual yields much lower than 99.73%. Smith continued to study yields and concluded that variation deteriorated (increased) over time. In other words, short-term performance, which was used to establish design standards, was higher than the long-term performance when actually producing a product. Through theoretical research and empirical study, Smith recognized this deterioration of variation was equivalent to about a 1.5 sigma shift in the mean. In other words, based upon short-term performance, long-term variation was about 1.5 sigma larger than short-term variation. The result was lower than expected yields, shorter reliability, and higher dissatisfaction from customers.

Smith's practical solution to this issue was to change the design band from the classical plus or minus three (3) short-term standard deviations from the target of the process, to plus or minus six (6) short-term standard deviations from the target of the process. This is where the term Six Sigma originated. In essence, the practical solution Smith developed was to double the design band of new product, so it would be robust to defects. This could be done either by reducing variation which in effect would decrease the process width or by increasing the specification limits. The preferred method was decreasing the process width through variation reduction which is why variation reduction became the focus of Six Sigma.

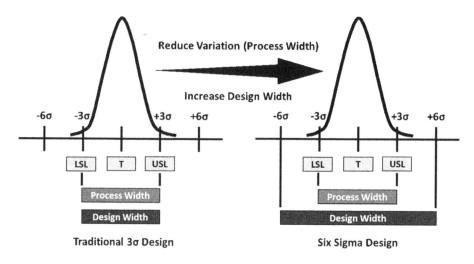

Figure 5 Understanding Variation Reduction

That is as technical as we are going to get in this book on the subject of variation reduction. Many Lean Six Sigma Black Belts and some Master Black Belts do not fully understand the concept of the 1.5 Sigma Shift. Setting aside the technical aspects of Smith's discoveries, your takeaway should be that processes deteriorate over time and that deterioration needs to be considered.

Success is achieved by focus. Focus is achieved through Project-by-Project Implementation.

Chapter 4
Project-by-Project Implementation

The first primary concept underlying Six Sigma was Variation Reduction and the second primary concept of Six Sigma and the focus of this book is The Breakthrough Strategy. But first, let's look at the third primary concept of Six Sigma, Project-by-Project Implementation.

The Project-by-Project Approach can be traced back to Joseph M. Juran's work in Quality. Juran believed that "the vital few chronic problems usually cut across department lines and required cross-functional 'project' teams" working on projects to resolve them. Juran believed this so strongly that he stated, "Improvement in organizations is accomplished on a project-by-project basis and in no other way." This is a frequently used quotation by Juran and is a leading quote in Richard Capper's book *A Project-By-Project Approach to Quality: A Practical Handbook for Individuals, Teams, and Organizations.*[6]

Mikel continued with the Project-by-Project approach in his development of Six Sigma by making projects the tool of implementation. While Mikel recognized the importance of cross-functional teams, he believed that projects should be led by skilled leaders who are highly trained in statistics and other important tools. These skilled project leaders were identified as Six Sigma Belts with color designations of black, green, yellow, and white which designated their skill level, like martial arts.

There is long-standing research that identifies "focus" as the most essential element of business success. Alice Schroeder, who wrote the biography of Warren Buffet entitled *The Snowball,*[7] recounts that when Warren Buffet first met Bill Gates at a dinner party, Gate's mother asked everyone around the table to share the single most important factor to their success. Both Gates and Buffet responded with the same one-word answer, **"Focus."**

Paraphrasing Greg McKeown, author of *Essentialism,*[8] the upside of true Focus is clear. You pursue a single objective and don't get distracted along the way;

you build momentum. In other words, you are determined to concentrate on one task, goal, or objective without distraction.

I also like the way McKeown identifies the phases of success:

Phase 1: When we have clarity of purpose, it leads to success.

Phase 2: When we have success, it leads to more options and opportunities.

Phase 3: When we have increased options and opportunities, it leads to diffused efforts.

Phase 4: Diffused efforts undermine the very clarity that led to our success in the first place.

McKeown's phases of success simply underline the importance of focus. Maintaining focus leads to success. Relaxing focus leads to diffused efforts.

Bobb Biehl,[9] a self-proclaimed Executive Mentor, says, "Without focusing and getting to clarity, you cannot lead. You cannot motivate. You cannot plan. You cannot communicate." Focus is not only important to success; it is a critical element of leadership.

There is no indication from the research that either Juran or Mikel cited "focus" as a reason to use the Project-by-Project Approach; however, it is clear they understood using this method led directly to focusing on one vital issue at a time. Beyond just focusing on a single vital issue, projects typically have time bounds. By setting time bounds on each project, project leaders and the team are forced to focus on reaching project objectives in a timely way.

> *We want to have breakthrough in everything that we do.*

Chapter 5
Origins of the Breakthrough Strategy

The remaining chapters of this section of the book will focus on the second primary concept underlying Six Sigma: The Breakthrough Strategy: The Six Sigma Way of Thinking.

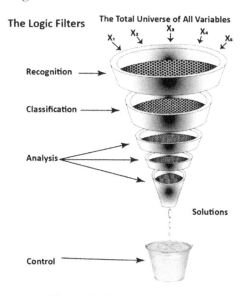

Figure 6 The Logic Filters

After receiving his master's degree in 1981, Mikel began to pursue a doctoral degree immediately. He was not content to enroll in just any doctoral program, but instead designed his program and submitted it to three schools. His program—which focused on industrial technology, technical education, research and experimental statistics, quantitative research design, and computer-intensive research methods—-was accepted by Arizona State University. It was during his doctoral work that Mikel developed a problem-solving methodology, a thought process he called The Logic Filters, which he finalized in 1983.

The Logic Filters model looked at the total of all variables in the universe and filtered them through Recognition, Classification, and Analysis to render desired solutions. The desired solutions were then put under a Control System to maintain their level of performance.

Mikel was a student of quality and leadership. The Logic Filters reflect what he learned from great quality leaders like Walter A. Shewhart, Joseph M. Juran, and W. Edwards Deming. As a doctoral intern at Motorola's GEG Radar Operations, Mikel had the opportunity to work with Dorian Shainin. Shainin is "most notable for his contributions in the fields of industrial problem solving, product reliability, and quality engineering, particularly the creation and development of the 'Red X' concept."[10]

Mikel's work is clearly rooted in Juran's 1964 book *Managerial Breakthrough: A New Concept of the Manager's Job*.[11] Juran believed that all management activity should be directed at either breakthrough or control. Juran noted that "Breakthrough is the creation of good change, or at least necessary change, whereas control is the prevention of bad change."

Juran goes on to note:

> Over the centuries "Our predecessors achieved breakthroughs by joining together three great ideas: 1) discovery of knowledge; 2) dissemination of this discovered knowledge to those who could use it; and 3) application of the new knowledge to the solution of old problems."

While Smith came up with the concept of establishing a plus or minus 6 sigma design band for making products robust to defects, it was Mikel who was charged with the task of implementing Smith's concept after his untimely death. Not surprisingly, from the beginning, Mikel's implementation was centered around The Logic Filters and his understanding of the importance of breakthrough. Mikel changed the name of The Logic Filters he developed earlier as part of his doctoral work to The Breakthrough Strategy, which was modified from Recognition, Classification, Analysis, and Control to MAIC: Measure, Analyze, Improve, Control.

Six Sigma was Mikel's catalyst. Six Sigma's success is what led to Mikel's recognition as a great thought leader. However, without The Breakthrough Strategy, Six Sigma is just the practice of doubling the design band so as to be robust to defects. It was really the implementation plan of The Breakthrough Strategy that brought Mikel's work to the forefront. It's just that it was buried under the name of Six Sigma.

Mikel worked on the concept of breakthrough from his doctoral days, starting with The Logic Filters up until his death in 2017. As noted, The Logic Filters became The Breakthrough Strategy, which came to be known as The Six Sigma Way of Thinking. The Breakthrough Strategy was Mikel's life's work, which he continued to develop and evolve through the four generations of Six Sigma.

In review, the three primary concepts of Six Sigma are: Variation Reduction, The Breakthrough Strategy, and Project-by-Project Implementation.

The first primary concept of Six Sigma is Bill Smith's concept of how variation reduction increases quality by making designs robust to defects and is the underlying factor of big problems.

The Breakthrough Strategy: The Six Sigma Way of Thinking, discussed in this chapter, is the second primary concept behind Six Sigma.

The third primary concept is Project-by-Project Implementation forming the underlying philosophy of Six Sigma with the concepts of Variation Reduction and Breakthrough. Both Juran and Mikel believed that the appropriate way to implement breakthrough was on a Project-by-Project basis.

We solve big problems through the strategy of Variation Reduction, using the Breakthrough Strategy, on a Project-by-Project basis. Variation Reduction is "What we want to do." The Breakthrough Strategy is the "Way we are going to do it." Project-by-Project Implementation is "How we are going to do it."

Knowledge involves belief, but not all belief is based upon knowledge.

Chapter 6
Building on the Foundation of Knowledge

Think back to when you first started in business, full of ideas and ready to conquer the world or at least the little world you were in at the time. You thought you had the most current knowledge, which you might have had. But you had little experience. You were anxious to make an impact. You were given your first project and excited about your solution. You presented your idea with enthusiasm, and as you walked away, you heard someone say, "How many times have we tried that?" One of our most significant faults as humans is that we don't want to take the time to discover what has been done before us.

I manufactured aerial work platforms (what many call "cherry pickers"), primarily for the aircraft industry. We were a small company, and our engineers had to be fluent in many disciplines: mechanical, electrical, fluid power, structural. Since most engineers were singularly disciplined, it took several years to develop them. I extended that development time by requiring them to first work in either Customer Service or Quality. I told them, "I want you to learn what kind of problems your decisions will create before you start applying your knowledge to solutions." I wanted them to understand the history of the task on which they were going to embark. I wanted them to have a baseline of performance before they started creating change.

I mentioned that Juran's *Managerial Breakthrough* had a copyright of 1964. Another great leader on management was Peter Drucker who, ten years earlier, wrote the book, *The Practice of Management*.[12] Drucker defined the purpose of an organization as "making common men into uncommon men." My management philosophy was similar: "Challenge people to do more than what they think they can and make them better than average." I tried to do this "one person at a time." Mikel stated his philosophy as: "Six Sigma is about transforming ordinary performance into extraordinary results, as common thinking simply brings common results." All of these statements have a common theme: the need to transform from common or average to something better.

Drucker taught us many things about management, but consider what he says about leadership. Drucker writes, "Leadership is of the utmost importance. But leadership cannot be created or promoted. It cannot be taught. Management cannot create leaders." A few sentences later, Drucker acknowledges: "Management can create the conditions under which potential leadership qualities become effective." His point is, we cannot create leaders, but we can help natural leaders become effective.

I agree that managers as leaders must create an environment in which others can grow as leaders or else potential leaders will not develop. However, Drucker's statement that "Management cannot create leaders," is often quoted today; but in fact, it is wrong. Dr. Mikel J. Harry's Breakthrough Strategy: The Six Sigma Way of Thinking provides a framework that allows management to not only create leaders, but to create an environment where leaders can develop into extraordinary leaders.

The Define filter was added to MAIC in the 1990s when Six Sigma was launched at GE. DMAIC is the most common form of The Breakthrough Strategy. In school, we are taught mostly to analyze and improve, with some minimal focus on measurement. We might be taught about the need for a control loop but typically we are not taught about Define, which is the need to establish a baseline before we start looking for a solution. To paraphrase Mikel, "We don't know what we don't know. If we don't understand the baseline, how are we going to evaluate whether or not we are creating beneficial change versus change for change's sake?"

We can't measure change to know if it is real if we don't define and measure the baseline, the current state condition. If we can't measure the change, how do we know how much impact, if any, the change made? We could have change with a negative impact and not know it. Just because we work hard and there is physical change does not mean there will be beneficial change in the results. If we do not have a baseline or don't measure the results, we have no idea if there was real change or not.

Six Sigma and the Breakthrough Strategy have stood the test of time. Mikel evolved it through four generations, strengthening the foundation with each generation. It is a proven, teachable, repeatable system that has led to extraordinary documented results. The Six Sigma Way of Thinking is the very foundation of Leadership and the framework for showing how to transform ordinary performance into extraordinary results. To be a leader and to teach others to be leaders, we only need to follow the recipe Mikel developed for us.

> *An assumption is merely a potential fact which is dependent upon faith.*
>
> ⟶

Chapter 7
Current State Six Sigma Defined

We have learned Six Sigma has evolved over four generations. We have learned Six Sigma's three primary components are Variation Reduction, The Breakthrough Strategy, and Project-by-Project Implementation.

We will learn a lot more about Six Sigma, but first I will attempt to answer the question "What is Six Sigma?" by looking at the two current state Six Sigma models. We'll look at Generation III which focuses on Value Entitlement for the customer and the provider (the Business Relationship or just simply Business), and we'll look at The Great Discovery which focuses on human achievement in everything we do.

> Six Sigma is a powerful, extraordinary, proactive way of thinking that combines with a series of "Big Ideas," leading to the satisfaction of values in any situation (business and personal) – Six Sigma is Leadership in your business and personal life.

Merriam-Webster Dictionary[13] defines leadership as 1) the office or position of a leader; 2) capacity to lead; 3) the act or instance of leading. *Thesaurus.com*[14] identifies the following as the most relevant synonyms for leadership: administration, authority, command, control, direction, influence, initiative, management, power, and skill.

Neither the dictionary nor the thesaurus provides a clear understanding of the word Leadership. Kevin Kruse, an author of several books on leadership, offers this definition: "Leadership is a process of social influence, which maximizes the efforts of others, towards the achievement of a goal."[15] The Breakthrough Strategy: The Six Sigma Way of Thinking is a process for changing ordinary thinking into extraordinary thinking. The Breakthrough Strategy: The Six Sigma Way of Thinking is synonymous with Leadership.

Let's discard Drucker's statement that "leaders cannot be created" and learn how The Six Sigma Way of Thinking can do just that. As noted previously, The

Breakthrough Strategy began with The Logic Filters and has had many forms. The most common is from the General Electric era of the 1990s, which is DMAIC: Define, Measure, Analyze, Improve, and Control. In its longest form, the Breakthrough Strategy is RDMAICSI: Recognize, Define, Measure, Analyze, Improve, Control, Standardize, and Integrate. It is through this longest form of The Breakthrough Strategy that we will develop a model that can be used to create and develop leaders. To better understand RDMAICSI, we will look at each of the phases individually.

Recognize

Recognition was the first filter in Mikel's original Logic Filters model. But what do we need to recognize? Looking back at The Logic Filters model in Figure 6, you can see that Mikel's Recognition filter was intended to take the total universe of variables and filter them so the important ones would be recognizable and the subject of a project, or Breakthrough Mission, that would lead to a solution. As Mikel's work continued, he came to understand that the driving force behind any Breakthrough Mission is *a need to satisfy our values.*

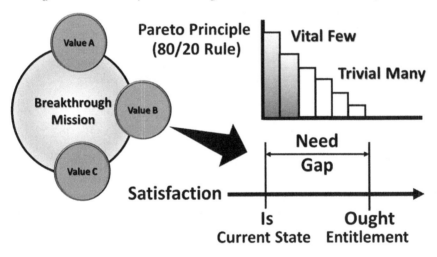

Figure 7 Need

Mikel defined Need as the gap between what ought to be (entitlement) and what is (the current condition). Mikel then adopted Juran's Pareto Principle (many may know this as the 80/20 rule) and said that we should focus breakthrough on the vital few needs (Figure 7).

We learned that Value Entitlement is the intersection between the customer and the provider: the business relationship. Business is created when both the customer and the provider see the potential to move from their current state of value satisfaction to an entitlement state of value satisfaction. In our personal life, once we see a potential to satisfy our values, we are motivated to take action.

The Recognize Phase of The Breakthrough Strategy implies we are looking at existing things, but in some cases, innovation may be required. Mikel introduced an innovation model that he called the ICRAtic Value Creation Strategy of Innovation, Configuration, Realization, and Attenuation, or ICRA for short, in Generation III Six Sigma (Figure 8).

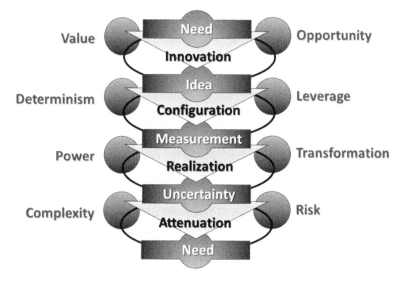

Figure 8 The ICRAtic Value Creation Strategy

ICRA was introduced when Mikel and Don Linsenmann of DuPont changed Six Sigma to be a focus on value creation, as opposed to Generation I, which focused on defects, and Generation II, where the focus was on cost reduction. Sadly, very few Six Sigma Belts have even heard the term ICRA, which indicates their knowledge of Six Sigma is more than a decade outdated.

Mikel and Linsenmann described this evolution in *The Six Sigma Fieldbook*. When compared to the original Logic Filter model, which filters the total universe of all variables, ICRA teaches us to search the universe of currently unknown variables to innovate—invent or create something new—which will bring higher levels of satisfaction. We can think of ICRA as a model for creating Breakthrough of what might be, whereas DMAIC is a model for creating Breakthrough in what is.

Mikel noted that thought begins with the strategic ideas of Innovation, Configuration, Realization, and Attenuation. We will look deeper into Innovation later, but for now we need to understand that there may be a need for innovation during the Recognize phase if we are unable to meet our needs with existing concepts or solutions.

So as leaders, what do we need to recognize? We need to recognize our values, what's important to us. In the event we don't know what is important to us, we need to use innovation skills to determine what is important to us or we will never be satisfied. Once we have identified our values, we need to determine the vital few opportunities that will give us the most leverage via a Breakthrough Mission to satisfy those values. We are trying to recognize both 'where we are' and 'where we need to be,' concerning satisfying our values.

DMAIC

We first filtered out all but the vital strategic needs that will give us the leverage in achieving breakthrough toward satisfying our values, which we call the "vital few." We then turn one or more of the vital few into projects which are documented with Project Charters. These Project Charters make a case for why the projects are something worthy of pursuing. The Project Charter outlines DMAIC (Define, Measure, Analyze, Improve, Control), the way we are going to attack the project, and sets time bounds for each of the DMAIC steps.

The relationship between DMAIC and the original Logic Filters is shown in Figure 9. Having recognized the need and promoting it to the level of a project, we now need to Define and Measure that need. Defining the need means we define and measure the baseline, or the current state, and we establish a quantifiable stretch goal, or what we'll call "the entitlement state."

Once we recognize the values and have determined our need by quantifying the baseline and setting an entitlement level through Define and Measure, we enter the Analyze phase. We analyze the need by searching through our bag of Big Ideas and determining what Six Sigma tools we will use to reduce the gap between entitlement and our current state: the Need.

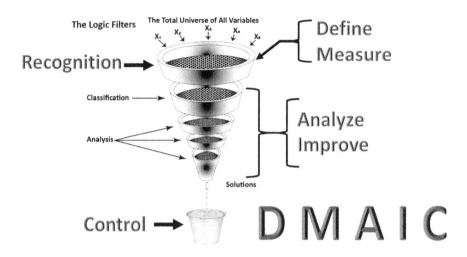

Figure 9 The Relationship Between DMAIC and The Logic Filters

Ideally, we would like to eliminate the gap to be consistent with the idea of perfection that will get us to full satisfaction. We need to be realistic and smart. The world is dynamic, not static. Tomorrow's conditions are not going to be the same as today's conditions. So rather than strive for perfection, which would be total elimination of the gap, why not aim for reducing it? We can apply the Pareto Principle, which says we can reduce 80% of the gap with 20% of the effort, while the remaining 20% of the gap will take 80% of the effort. Reducing the gap by 80% may reveal other needs that have more leverage, in which case we should change our focus and concentrate on those. We want always to stay focused on what gives us the most leverage at the strategic level.

In the original Logic Filters, DMAIC was a combination of Classification and Analysis. In DMAIC, the classification of problems is what guides us in the Analysis phase regarding what ideas and tools we need to use. Improvement did not exist in the original Logic Filters. Instead, Analysis led directly to solutions.

People drive themselves crazy trying to describe down to the gnat's level where the breakpoint is between Define and Measure and between Analyze and Improve. In the original Logic Filters, Analyze would have been a combination of Analyze and Improve. The need gap would be analyzed, and we would use that analysis to come up with an improvement strategy to meet our stretch goals.

Mikel and I would likely not have agreed on my thinking regarding how to apply DMAIC. In contrast to Mikel, I combine Define and Measure. I view Analysis as terminating with a proposed improvement plan. Improvement then becomes the task of implementing the improvement plan. While my method is consistent with Mikel's original Logic Filters, Mikel was adamant that each of the five phases of DMAIC were to be treated distinctly and separately. I'm sure Mikel and I would have agreed to disagree. The point is that it doesn't matter how you apply DMAIC. Just make sure each step gets done.

Control has to do with establishing a monitor-and-trigger system to alert us when breakthrough improvement projects are no longer on track. It takes a lot to break a habit. We don't want to stay attached to the project for as long as it takes for a habit to change. So, we must have a control system to ensure that the "improved way" becomes the habit without us being present. And we must consciously ensure it is done the way we want every time.

Standardize and Integrate

We previously introduced ICRA, or what Mikel called the ICRAtic Value Creation Strategy, which consists of Innovation, Configuration, Realization, and Attenuation. I know all the acronyms and strategies get to be a bit overwhelming but bear with me for a bit longer.

The last step of ICRA is Attenuate. Mikel defined Attenuate as reducing the size, strength, or destiny of something. Standardize and Integrate are additional filters applied after the need has been recognized, and those needs are leveraged and controlled through DMAIC. We can think of Standardize and Integrate as the filters for attenuating future risk (Figure 10).

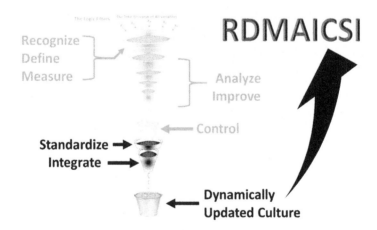

Figure 10 Standardize and Integrate Dynamically Updated Culture

The Standardize filter is where we communicate successes and maintain a database of lessons learned, so that we don't keep learning the same lessons over and over. The Integrate filter is where we take the knowledge acquired and turn it into a general policy that will guide future decisions. By integrating our gained knowledge into policy, we can change our culture, change what we believe. Changing what we believe will attenuate future risks as we go to new rounds of Recognize.

With RDMAICSI (Recognize, Define, Measure, Analyze, Improve, Control, Standardize, Integrate), which we will refer to as the Expanded Breakthrough Strategy, we now have a leadership strategy and way of thinking that creates Breakthrough in everything upon which we focus. With these tools, we are now able to dynamically and continuously update our culture.

To improve means we must be able to predict and prevent, not detect and react.

Chapter 8
Evolution of the Breakthrough Strategy

Mikel's original Logic Filters model had three filters: Recognition, Classification, and Analysis. When these filters were applied to a universe of all variables, the result was a solution which was then placed under Control.

When Mikel was asked to implement Smith's "plus or minus six (6) sigma design band concept" at Motorola to make products robust to defects, he modified The Logic Filters model, as the Recognition filter was not needed. Motorola executive Art Sundry made the problem clear when he stood up in an executive meeting and proclaimed, "The real problem at Motorola is our quality stinks!"[16] It was also presumed, since Motorola recognized a need for change, that upper management could easily "recognize" other needs in the organization required to satisfy their values. As a result, the Recognition filter was dropped. Additionally, Mikel understood the importance of measuring the current state condition to determine the impact of change objectively. Therefore, the Measure phase was added to replace the Recognition filter. The Analysis filter was replaced with Analyze and Improve, indicating a need for action on the analysis to realize results. These modifications resulted in The Logic Filters being transformed at Motorola to a new model, The Breakthrough Strategy: MAIC – Measure, Analyze, Improve, Control.

When Six Sigma was launched at General Electric, the focus was on cost reduction, as opposed to quality focus at Motorola. However, the cost reduction projects were quite diverse, so the Define step was added to narrow the scope of the macro problem. Thus, the Breakthrough Strategy changed from MAIC at Motorola to DMAIC (Define, Measure, Analyze, Improve, Control) at General Electric. DMAIC is the most recognizable form of the Breakthrough Strategy. DMAIC is the tactical portion of the Expanded Breakthrough Strategy of RDMAICSI and is the focus of most of the training for Six Sigma Belts.

We mentioned that when Six Sigma was deployed at DuPont, the focus changed once again. At DuPont, the focus was on growth under the concept that the customer and the provider realize value in every critical aspect of the business relationship. If that business relationship improves by increasing the satisfaction of values for both the customer and the provider, then the business grows. Mikel liked to say, at DuPont, the focus of Six Sigma changed from "The business of Quality" to the "Quality of Business." Mikel was proud that Six Sigma had successfully evolved from a quality improvement initiative to a full-fledged business initiative. While Mikel used the word "evolve" to describe the migration of the generations of Six Sigma it might be better said that Mikel was wise and flexible enough to adapt and expand his model from the specific focus on quality to a focus on all aspects of business, depending on need. Upon completing this book, you should understand that in fact, Mikel's "Thought Models" are adaptable to any situation. They simply form the way we should think as Leaders.

It is not clear when, but sometime after the General Electric deployment in the 1990s, Mikel expanded the Breakthrough Strategy from DMAIC to RDMAICSI (Recognize, Define, Measure, Analyze, Improve, Control, Standardize, Integrate) which we introduced previously as the current version of the Breakthrough Strategy. This expanded version of the Breakthrough Strategy is documented in Mikel's best-selling book, written with Richard Schroeder, called *Six Sigma: The Breakthrough Management Strategy Revolutionizing the World's Top Organizations*.[17] Mikel liked to refer to this book as *The Blue Book*. It is clear then that RDMAICSI evolved somewhere between the General Electric and DuPont deployments.

At DuPont, two strategies were used. ICRA which was introduced previously as an innovation model for focusing on value creation, and the Expanded Breakthrough Strategy of RDMAICSI which was used as an implementation strategy. Mikel was big on classification and working in pairs: Four pairs of two was his favorite structure. In Mikel's *The Blue Book*, he groups the eight phases of RDMAICSI into four stages: Identification, Characterization, Optimization, and Institutionalization (Figure 11).

The Identification stage consists of the Recognize and Define phases with the objective of identifying key business issues that would satisfy values. The Characterization stage consists of Measure and Analyze with the objective of understanding current performance levels and establishing a baseline or current state condition, setting stretch entitlement goals, and employing Six Sigma tools and Big Ideas to determine how the need gap can be reduced. The Optimization stage consists of Improve and Control with the objective of achieving breakthrough improvement and maintaining the improvement until it becomes a habit. The Institutionalization stage consists of Standardize and Integrate with the objective of transforming how day-to-day business should be conducted.

Stages	Phases	Objective
Identification	Recognize Define	Identify key business issues
Characterization	Measure Analyze	Understand current performance levels
Optimization	Improve Control	Achieve Breakthrough Improvement
Institutionalization	Standardize Integrate	Transform how to do day-to-day business

Figure 11 Expanded Breakthrough Strategy

It is not clear when, but sometime between the publication of *The Blue Book* in the year 2000 and the development of Mikel's MindPro[18] Lean Six Sigma training in 2003, the Institutionalization stage of Standardize and Integrate was renamed the Validation Stage, making ICOV the acronym for the four stages of The Breakthrough Strategy (Figure 12). The four stages of ICOV which expand to eight phases of RDMAICSI is the current Breakthrough Model. As with ICRA, most Belts have never heard the term ICOV, which reflects their need to update their Six Sigma knowledge.

	Stages	Phases	Objective
I	Identification	Recognize Define	Identify key business issues
C	Characterization	Measure Analyze	Understand current performance levels
O	Optimization	Improve Control	Achieve Breakthrough Improvement
V	Validation	Standardize Integrate	Transform how to do day-to-day business

Figure 12 ICOV Model of RDMAICSI

The Great Discovery shows you how anyone or any team can achieve breakthrough in pursuit of their personal dreams and business goals.

Chapter 9
The Great Discovery

The Great Discovery is known as Generation IV of Six Sigma and is a personal model for the Breakthrough Strategy: The Six Sigma Way of Thinking. The genesis for The Great Discovery started after the Generation II launch at General Electric in the 1990s. Jack Welch, CEO of General Electric, said, "Six Sigma is the most important initiative GE has ever undertaken... it is part of the genetic code of our future leadership."[19] Mikel had led the transformation at GE and had trained many Champions and Belts. Welch challenged Mikel further when he asked, "What about the other 95% of my employees?" Mikel had to answer simply, "I don't know." Jacques Nasser, former Ford President and CEO, commented to Mikel after Ford's successful deployment, "If you could just teach us how you think." The comments from Welch and Nasser gnawed at Mikel.

From our best estimates, Mikel started working on The Great Discovery around 2005. Mikel was good about keeping his projects secret even from those he trusted. Looking back, I have email correspondence from 2007 in which Mikel and I discussed parts of what would become The Great Discovery. The first training session for The Great Discovery was in 2009. In 2010, Mikel and Cathy Lawson authored *The Great Discovery: A Process That Creates Breakthrough In Everything You Do*.[20] The objective of The Great Discovery was to answer Welch's and Nasser's questions. Mikel writes in the Forward of the book, "In a nutshell, The Great Discovery is a process that advances human achievement to the point of breakthrough... and beyond."

We noted previously that Generation III Six Sigma, based on the ICOV model of RDMAICSI, is the current model for the Breakthrough Strategy. Since The Great Discovery is Generation IV, where does it fit?

Generation III, the ICOV model of RDMAICSI, is considered the current state commercial model for The Six Sigma Way of Thinking. Generation IV, The Great Discovery, is regarded as the current state personal model for The Six Sigma Way of Thinking. In fact, both are current state models for The Breakthrough Strategy: The Six Sigma Way of Thinking—one commercial and one personal.

One of the most essential things to Mikel as he built The Great Discovery was to move away from statistics and technical terms associated with Six Sigma and use a common language that could be understood by everyone. Many people have math or technology phobia, and just the mention of statistics or technical terms is enough to drive them away. Mikel was mindful of this phobia and did not want to scare these people away. He kept this in mind as he developed the model.

The four stages of The Great Discovery are: Do the Dreaming, Dream the Doing, Plan the Doing, and Do the Plan. Earlier, we mentioned Mikel's fascination with pairs and classification. Mikel grouped the four stages of The Great Discovery into two pairs. The first pair, he labeled Innovation consisting of the two stages: Do the Dreaming and Dream the Doing. The second pair he labeled Execution consisting of the two stages: Plan the Doing and Do the Plan.

Figure 13 The Great Discovery Model

Mikel went on to break the four stages down into eight steps, as shown in Figure 13 The Do the Dreaming stage consists of Clarify Core Values and Determine Catalyst Dream. The Dream the Doing stage consists of Establish

Leading Milestones and Select Problematic Milestones. Plan the Doing consists of Identify Vital Forces and Define Enabling Actions. And Do the Plan consists of Complete Action Plan and Check Progress Results.

Only those of us close to Mikel understand how hard he worked to get The Great Discovery model into four stages broken into eight steps. Mikel's stubbornness regarding his fascination with the four-stage/eight-step model becomes apparent when studying the details of The Great Discovery model.

The eight steps of The Great Discovery model replaced the DMAIC portion of the ICOV model of RDMAICSI. Mikel recognized he still needed to deal with Recognize, Standardize, and Integrate from the ICOV model. Rather than break up the four-stage/eight-step model, Mikel added the two steps in an unusual way. He added a Step Zero of Declare Improvement Mission, which becomes part of the Innovation categorization. And he added an asterisk step at the end, which is Document Lessons Learned. While it's not part of Mikel's The Great Discovery Model, I like to add a second asterisk step of Update The Way You Think.

The great discovery Breakthrough Strategy

Declare Improvement Mission

Do the Dreaming

Innovation

Clarify Core Values

Determine Catalyst Dream

Dream the Doing

Establish Leading Milestones

Select Problematic Milestones

Identify Vital Forces

Plan the Doing

Define Enabling Actions

Execution

Complete Action Plan

Do the Plan

Check Progress Results

Document Lessons Learned

Update The Way You Think

Figure 14 The Great Discovery Expanded Model

I like to look at the stages of The Great Discovery from the following perspective:

Stage 1: Dream the Doing is about "What we want to achieve."

Stage 2: Do the Dreaming is about "How we are going to get there."

Stage 3: Plan the Doing is about "Finding the forces that have leverage."

Stage 4: Do the Plan is about "Executing in a timely way."

As Mikel said, "In a nutshell, The Great Discovery is a process that advances human achievement to the point of breakthrough… and beyond."

Like the ICOV model of RDMAICSI, The Great Discovery is a highly structured, disciplined, systematic way of thinking that allows you to form a breakthrough dream or stretch goal, and then create a clear roadmap to the realization of these aspirations. We noted previously that The Breakthrough Strategy: The Six Sigma Way of Thinking is synonymous with Leadership. The Great Discovery is a way to provide leadership thinking not only for the 5% who are the best of the best, fluent in statistics, and with a tool belt of technical tools, but for the other 95%. In other words, by presenting it in straightforward terms, we can all understand and follow.

Figure 15 is a simplified version of The Great Discovery and provides a visual representation of the relationship between the Values, The Breakthrough Mission, the Catalyst, and the Milestones. As we noted, the need to fully satisfy our core values whether as an individual or an organization is our driving force. Our desire to fully satisfy our core values from an individual perspective can be considered our "Life's Dream." From an organization perspective our core values are represented in our long-term strategic plan. Our desire to completely satisfy the objectives of the long-term strategic plan could be considered our "Organization Dream." Whether a "Life Dream" or an "Organization Dream," the dream can be represented as a "Breakthrough Mission" for satisfying all values fully.

Once core values are determined, priorities are established for improving those values. This is the Recognize phase of the ICOV model of RDMAICSI. Those priorities are then turned into projects. In The Great Discovery, projects are called Catalysts. Projects or Catalysts link actions to values in a direct cause and effect way, in order to accomplish the Breakthrough Mission, the dream of moving values closer to entitlement. It is recognized that no single project or

Catalyst is going to bring all values to entitlement, so there will be a need for multiple projects or Catalysts in parallel or serially.

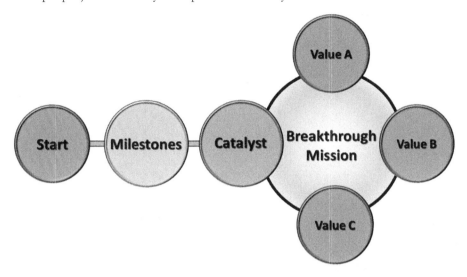

Figure 15 Values – Breakthrough Mission – Catalyst – Milestones

Each Catalyst is broken down into Milestones, a strategy of divide and conquer. When all of your focus is on the endpoint, no matter how great the dream may be, it is often hard to visualize how you will get there. In breaking the journey down into prioritized Catalysts and then breaking each Catalyst into critical milestones, you have divided the journey of full Value Entitlement into measurable steps that allow you to visualize the map to accomplishing your dream more easily. The accomplishment of the Catalyst can be considered mission success, in a chain of milestones focused on a specific element of the Breakthrough Mission. Similarly, completion of each milestone can be regarded as mission success for that part of the journey related to the accomplishment of a particular Catalyst.

We noted previously that the Do the Dreaming stage of The Great Discovery consists of Step 1: Clarify Core Values and Step 2: Determine Catalyst Dream. We also noted in our discussion on Recognition that Mikel came to understand that the driving force behind any Breakthrough Mission is the need to satisfy our core values.

The Breakthrough Strategy should be of importance to any forward-thinking leader who wants to enhance their ability to drive change.

Chapter 10
Comparing the Current State
Breakthrough Strategy Models

The two Breakthrough Strategy models of the ICOV model of RDMAICSI and The Great Discovery have been noted to be the current state models for The Six Sigma Way of Thinking. ICOV is considered a commercial model focused on Value Entitlement for the customer and provider, a focus which Mikel simply labeled Business. The Great Discovery is considered a personal model focused on human achievement. The Great Discovery reflects Mikel's latest thinking, so we will use it as the foundation of our comparison.

Recall that The Great Discovery starts with two broad categorizations: Innovation and Execution (Figure 13). Innovation breaks down into the stages of Do the Dreaming and Dream the Doing, which in turn break down into four steps: Clarify Core Values, Determine Catalyst Dream, Establish Leading Milestones, and Select Problematic Milestones. Remember, we have a Step zero, which is Declare the Improvement Mission and an asterisk step of Document Lessons Learned. In addition, I added another asterisk step: Update The Way You Think.

Two issues arise when comparing the ICOV model of RDMAICSI to The Great Discovery (Figure 16):

1. The ICOV model of RDMAICSI has no official Innovation and Execution categorization like The Great Discovery.

2. The Great Discovery does not have an official Validation categorization.

While not official in Mikel's original models, Innovation, Execution, and Validation are present in both models.

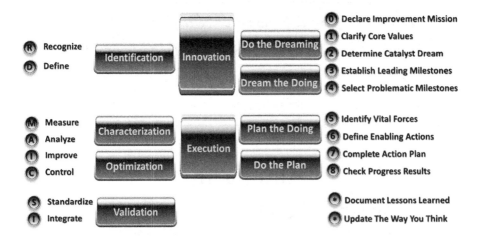

Figure 16 Comparing ICOV and The Great Discovery

The ICOV stage of Identification consists of the Recognize and Define phases which are Innovation steps. They correlate to The Steps in The Great Discovery Model, consisting of Declare Improvement Mission, Clarify Core Values, Determine Catalyst Dream, Establish Leading Milestones, and Select Problematic Milestones.

The Execution part of The Great Discovery consists of Plan the Doing and Do the Plan. Plan the Doing breaks down into the two steps of Identify Vital Forces and Define Enabling Actions. Do the Plan breaks down into the steps of Complete Action Plan and Check Progress Results. In the first deployment of Six Sigma at Motorola, the MAIC phases were Execution activities. Likewise, the execution stages of the ICOV model of RDMAICSI are Characterization and Optimization which breakdown into MAIC.

The ICOV model adds the phases of Standardize and Integrate to the Validation stage which is not specifically identified in The Great Discovery model. However, the asterisk step of Document Lessons Learned and the asterisk step that I added of Update The Way You Think, in fact, form a Validation stage.

Now let's take a closer look at The Great Discovery. Specifically, I want to look at Do the Dreaming and Dream the Doing. I want to ignore the four steps of Clarify Core Values, Determine Catalyst Dream, Establish Leading Milestones, and Select Problematic Milestones and just focus on the two stages Do the Dreaming and Dream the Doing. When Mikel used the word "Dream" in these two stages of The Great Discovery, he incorporated the concept of Visualization. The concept of Visualization is not present in the ICOV model of

RDMAICSI. The addition of Visualization to The Great Discovery was a breakthrough in Mikel's thinking.

Right after Mikel shared his completed version of The Great Discovery with me, I started sharing it, mostly with Lean Six Sigma Master Black Belts and Champions who were in my network. I thought they would be blown away about a product that could teach The Six Sigma Way of Thinking to the other 95%. Their response was not only underwhelming, many just laughed and said, "The Great Discovery it isn't."

I continued to share The Great Discovery, but now mostly with people that were not familiar with Six Sigma. I recall my doctor saying, "That is the exact technique I used when I decided to go back to school and become a doctor." I got similar responses as I continued to share The Great Discovery with successful people not familiar with Six Sigma.

What is the difference between the two groups? The Six Sigma people saw no value in The Great Discovery, and the lay group found it was a tool with which they were very familiar and one that was important to their success. Mikel always liked to say, "You don't know what you don't know." I think in the case of the Lean Six Sigma practitioners, "They didn't know what they knew." They were so into the technical aspects that The Great Discovery was just too simple for them. In the case of the lay group, what I came to realize was that The Great Discovery is a natural method used by successful people. These successful people typically are not able to verbalize or write down exactly how they think, but as soon as they see it in writing, they recognize it.

Working with my editor, Barb Smith, she relayed a story about a business friend named Larry. He was a work colleague and the company's top salesperson. Wanting to learn what made Larry successful, Barb made an effort to make the most of what she referred to as "windshield time" spent with Larry, driving from client to client. Paraphrasing Larry's observation about his success, as Barb communicated it to me:

> Barbara, you have to understand that not all people think as we do. Imagine that our minds are like a refrigerator door. You and I have everything – all our little sticky notes and lists and reminders – stuck up on that door, all nice and orderly in groups, but most people just stick stuff on the refrigerator door in random order. My success is that I understand that most people aren't able to organize their thoughts as you and I do, so I figure out how to communicate with them in a way they can understand.

As we have seen, The Great Discovery and the ICOV model of RDMAICSI are one and the same, even though the Lean Six Sigma experts couldn't or wouldn't recognize this. What Mikel was able to do with The Great Discovery was to break down the ICOV model into a natural process that is familiar to most successful people. By documenting this process in the form of The Great Discovery, Mikel developed a system that allows us to teach ***Anybody*** to think like a leader, even though their natural way of thinking might be like that disorganized refrigerator door.

Chapter 11
The Importance of Visualization

We noted that Mikel added the Visualization steps Do the Dreaming and Dream the Doing to The Great Discovery and that successful lay people identified visualization as being their key to success. We also noted that Visualization was not part of the ICOV model of RDMAICSI. I never discussed with Mikel why he added the Visualization step to The Great Discovery, as it just seemed natural to me. Just as for most successful people, the Visualization step was natural to Mikel as well. It's unclear if Mikel intentionally added Visualization or if it was added as part of Mikel's desire to get the ICOV Model of RDMAICSI down to a model that laypeople could understand. Regardless, the addition of Visualization was a breakthrough in The Six Sigma Way of Thinking.

Visualization has its roots in the Law of Attraction, also known as "New Thought" from the late 1800's. Ralph Waldo Trine, noted philosopher, author, and teacher, wrote in *In Tune With The Infinite*[21] in 1897:

> The law of attraction works universally on every plane of action, and we attract whatever we desire or expect. If we desire one thing and expect another, we become like houses divided against themselves, which are quickly brought to desolation. Determine resolutely to expect only what you desire, and then you will attract only what you wish for.

Mikel says in The Great Discovery, "You bring about what you think about." This is a straightforward way to state the Law of Attraction.

Jennice Vilhauer, Ph.D. wrote in *Psychology Today*,[22] "Your brain is constantly using visualization in the process of simulating future experiences, but this process happens so naturally that you generally aren't even aware of it, the same way you usually aren't aware that you are breathing. If you aren't aware of it, then you aren't actively directing the process."

Vilhauer noted there are two types of visualization: outcome and process. Outcome visualization is a sensory-based representation of the final result you expect. And process visualization involves simulating the steps that get you to the final result. She also noted you should visualize from a participant perspective as opposed to an observer perspective.

In The Great Discovery, Mikel noted the importance of separating the image of standing on the podium in victory from the journey taken to get to the podium. Visualizing yourself standing on the podium is fun. But dreaming about the path to get to the podium will lead you to a successful journey and change your dream from a pipe dream to an accomplished dream. In Mikel's words, it is crucial to spend the time envisioning the details needed to achieve the dream, visualizing the Catalyst, and the milestones needed to get there.

Once you imprint an idea in your brain, your mind starts triggering impulses and you begin to notice the thing you imprinted in your visual world. By thinking positively, the actions you take are often easier. The Visualization step differentiates extraordinary thinking from ordinary thinking.

Let's think about the process. Think about what Catalyst will move you closer to Value Entitlement. Think about what journey you will take to accomplish that Catalyst. Think about standing on that podium of success and how it will make you feel. Now for the hard part: look for a starting point. Don't look for excuses; look forward and make a commitment to achieve success. Once you start your journey, accomplishing each step will provide motivation and enthusiasm. Visualize standing on the starting line and what it is going to feel like when you reach your Catalyst.

Visualize the commitment required to seek change, what it will take to start the journey, and how it will feel once the journey is complete. Even though the journey is only in your mind at this point, you should be feeling proud, motivated, and that the dream is possible. When things get tough, stop and go through this visualization process again. Visualizing accomplishing each step provides the motivation and enthusiasm to maintain the pursuit.

Continue along the journey in your mind from milestone to milestone. As you reach each milestone in your mind, play back the journey you have traveled. By playing the journey back in your mind after each visualized success until you reach the podium, you will reinforce the idea that the dream is possible. When you finally see yourself on the podium with your hands raised in victory, you will feel confident that you can succeed.

In his book *Thinking, Fast and Slow*,[23] Daniel Kahneman breaks thinking into two processes. The fast way of thinking is intuitive, emotional, reactionary, and experientially based. Fast thinking is the type of thinking we do automatically. The slow way of thinking is more deliberate and more logical; it is reflective and reasoned. Slow thinking is something we must invoke and make a priority. We are going to focus on "slow thinking"– deeper thinking.

When I traveled to the Phoenix area to work with Mikel, I would stay at his home. The image of Mikel that is burned in my mind is of him sitting on the back porch in a trance-like state, thinking and running an idea over and over in his mind, desiring that the result would be something revolutionizing. I knew that what we had discussed yesterday was being run through the filter of Mikel's mind over and over. I also knew when we began to work that day, Mikel would be questioning everything we had discussed the day before, and we would likely be modifying our path toward a better outcome.

Deep thinking played an important role in the relationship I had with Mikel and the quality of work we developed. Mikel and I did most of our work by telephone, which was often half or three-quarter day conversations. It normally went something like this:

> Mikel would have an idea and want to talk about it. I'm sure that by the time he called me, he had already spent tens of hours on the back porch in deep thought. For the most part, Mikel would call me to validate what he already had down rock solid in his mind. Mikel would go on and on in great detail, rationalizing every angle. I'm a visual learner which made absorbing Mikel's thoughts by telephone difficult. I would furiously take notes, trying to convert his thoughts to something visual I could understand.

Inevitably, I would get to the point of brain overload before Mikel was done. I would interrupt Mikel and tell him I needed some absorption time, and I would need to call him back the next day. I know what happened on my end after hanging up the telephone. I would retreat to my little pond and go into a trance-like state thinking about all Mikel had to say. I would try to visualize what Mikel was telling me and try to visualize the path he was taking to get to his conclusion. I didn't need my notes, as just by writing them, I could visualize every minute of our conversation. I do not doubt that Mikel retreated to his back porch to refine his thoughts even further, by running them through progressively finer and finer filters. Deep thinking was embedded in our process.

When we think about the Visualization step in The Breakthrough Strategy, we must think about using deep thinking. We need to visualize and walk in our mind every step along the journey to success, looking out for anything that might detract from our success, and looking for things we can leverage to get us from milestone to milestone. At each milestone, we also need to play back the journey we have traveled and the achievements we have made.

In my book, *Passion in the Wind. Dream, Believe, and Achieve the Extraordinary,*[24] I document a 23,000-mile motorcycle ride in which my friend Tim Yow and I, both in our 60s, circumnavigated the United States and Canada. As you might guess from the subtitle, you will find a reference in the book to The Great Discovery. Before embarking on this adventure, I had visualized it many times as I pondered over maps, road and weather conditions, ferry schedules, availability of gasoline, and other issues which might impact our trip. I was confident Tim and I would be successful in our mission.

Figure 17 Eagle Plains
Left to Right: Alan Leduc, Tim Yow, Harry Farthing, Steven Kurowski

Regardless of our planning, Tim and I found ourselves at Eagle Plains, Northwest Territories, Canada where we were advised that the ice roads were late in thawing and the ferry was not able to operate across the river. We would not be able to go any further. However, there was a possibility the ferry would be able to operate the next day. There was not much of an alternative but to spend the night at the only hotel and gas station within 250 miles. This is an excerpt from my book:

> As fate would have it, two other adventurers were hanging around the hotel: Harry Farthing and Steven Kurowski.
>
> Steven is standing next to his bicycle. Yes, a bicycle! Steven had an uncle and a high school classmate who both died of cancer. Even though he was overweight and out of shape, Steven decided he would ride his bicycle across Canada in an attempt to raise one million dollars

for cancer research. Steven was quoted in the Dawson Creek Daily News as saying, "My uncle's battle took him piece by piece. My friend, on the other hand, went to the doctor one day and found out he had terminal cancer and died very quickly." Steven himself found out that he is in a pre-cancer stage of colon cancer. He doesn't have cancer yet but must monitor his condition.

Steven rides several hours a day, only stopping for short power-rests, for a coffee, food, and sleep. His trip started in Vancouver, and the first phase of his trip ended in October 2011 in Quebec where he planned to stay for the winter. At the time this was written, Steven planned to start riding again in the Spring and complete the trip by riding to St. John's Newfoundland, which will take another four months.

Harry is an accomplished mountaineer and former managing partner of Cushman & Wakefield, a global real estate company. Harry climbed to the peaks of Kilimanjaro and Mount Denali, and in 2006, he nearly peaked Mount Everest. Harry had spent six years planning his attempt at the world's highest peak, but at the balcony (8,500 meters), he was dealing with concerns about repeat frostbite in his fingers and feet and decided he didn't have enough strength left to ensure a safe descent.

In Harry's own words: "I have given it absolutely everything I have got. After 12 trips through the Khumbu Icefall, around 200 ladder crossings, and four round trips on the mountain to 6,100 meters, 6,400 meters, 7,000 meters, and 8,500 meters, I can at least say I have climbed Mount Everest, even if I didn't summit. I am alive, well, and still have ten fingers and toes. The summit was always the bonus."

Like Steven, Harry used his endeavors for charity. He made many of his climbs for his company's charity, Schools Around the World. Harry, a Brit with an American wife and daughter, recently moved to North Carolina and was riding his motorcycle to Alaska, where he would once again visit Denali, this time to reminisce and not climb.

Since we were stranded and it was early afternoon, the four of us struck up a conversation in the hotel lounge. Steven's and Harry's reactions were similar to those of the gentleman I talked to on the ferry to Victoria Island. He had sailed a boat to Fiji but thought riding 800 miles a day on a motorcycle seemed dangerous. We all were enamored by each other's challenges.

As our discussion went through dinner, we came to realize that while each of our challenges was uniquely different, we approached them the same. Tim and I had a daily goal but made decisions one tank of gas at a time. Steven had developed an itinerary and simply focused on making it to his next stop. Harry's focus was one portion of the mountain at a time and, as the climb neared the end, one step at a time. We realized that we had more in common than we had differences.

Like with the motorcycle adventure, process-based visualization allowed me to accomplish another feat which I never dreamed possible – running a half-marathon. My friend, Barb Smith, who I first met through motorcycling, runs half-marathons several times a year. Coincidently, Barb was the editor for my book *Passion in the Wind* and is also the editor for this book.

I was recovering from foot surgery in 2012 and was doing a lot of treadmill work as part of my path to recovery. Barb posted something on one of the social media sites about an upcoming half-marathon and it triggered something in my brain that made me wonder if I could do something like that. I had never been a runner and now at age 62, it seemed like an unimaginable challenge; but Barb's passion and my desire to not have long-term effects from the foot surgery inspired me.

Barb's response was "Why not?" She recounted that when she trains for and does a half-marathon, she just breaks it down into little pieces and visualizes getting to the next piece, one piece at a time, be it adding incremental miles to each training run, or reaching a mile marker, water station, or something else along the route on race day. As Barb noted, when I did my first long distance motorcycle ride, I just applied this same technique and was confident I could do it.

She said, "You are a long-distance motorcycle rider, so just break down the run, just like you break down your motorcycle rides."

In 2013, I completed a half-marathon with Barb in Anchorage, Alaska. I still consider this one of the greatest accomplishments of my life. The point of this personal story is that using deep thinking and process-based visualization of the journey in the role of the participant seems to be a natural phenomenon for extraordinary accomplishment.

As an executive, one of my most important roles was to encourage deep thinking in others. I knew when someone sought assistance from me, they wanted or needed an answer right then. An immediate response would mean they were going to get a response from my fast thinking. They knew their job better than I did, so rather than answer intuitively, I would usually ask, "What do you think you should do?" I knew they likely had the answer; they just needed to dig for it.

Interestingly, my CEO told me once that he had never seen me answer questions from any of my employees. He was bothered by what he perceived as my unwillingness to provide appropriate guidance. I had to explain my rationale to him. I'm not sure he ever got it.

As an educator, I remember disagreeing with the author of a textbook during a lecture. A student raised a hand and said, "Who are you to disagree with the author. He is an expert." When we fail to challenge what others have to say or, more importantly, test our own fast-thinking response, we are not reaching our full potential. Many take facts, statistics, and other information, but never question what is behind them. I'm sure that my students didn't fully appreciate it at the time, but I would manipulate equations every algebraic way possible and usually end with, "You should now be able to write your own equation." I wanted them to understand the concept, not memorize the equation.

Visualization must be combined with slow thinking, deep thinking, in order to deliver the best outcome. Visualization and deep thinking are critical elements in The Six Sigma Way of Thinking.

Since Visualization is not part of the ICOV model of RDMAICSI, should we add a Visualization step to ICOV?

The difference between those trained with the commercial ICOV model of RDMAICSI and those trained with the personal model of The Great Discovery, is that those trained with the commercial model have many more tools and techniques on their tool belts. They are the 5% who are presumed to be the best of the best and presumed to be leaders already.

In the commercial world, almost all critical projects are handled by teams. We encourage the use of cross-functional teams to solve problems and lead change management. Cross-functional teams provide expanded intellectual power, experience, and diverse thinking. The teams use brainstorming, cause and effect diagrams, affinity diagrams, and many other tools that encourage the team members to play off each other to dig deeper into the problem in search of better solutions.

In The Great Discovery, we are encouraged to put together a Dream Team, a team that is invested in us and wants to see us succeed. However, in most cases, this will be more of an emotional support team, our cheerleaders that help keep us motivated. They may be our family and friends who want us to succeed in our mission of achieving an education goal, meeting a health goal, or some other goal. They may care about us achieving our dream genuinely, but they are not accountable for achieving the goal like a cross-functional commercial team.

While in the personal model of The Great Discovery, Visualization via Do the Dreaming and Dream the Doing is vital as a formal part of the process, and even though Visualization is beneficial to the ICOV model, it should not be added as a formal Visualization stage. Like so many of the Six Sigma tools, Visualization is not phase-specific. It is a tool we should use in every phase of RDMAICSI. We should consider Visualization, not as an added stage, but as another tool that is hooked on our tool belt. We should incorporate Visualization in the way we lead by allowing time for it in every critical decision to be made.

Imagine instead of ending a meeting with a proposed solution, we ended the meeting with "Each of you go back and visualize the journey we have defined. Visualize the work that will be required. Visualize the roadblocks that we may encounter. Visualize how we are going to succeed and how we might fail. Visualize each step along our journey to successful resolution. Think about this deeply. Let's get back together tomorrow and see if we can come up with an even better solution." I bet that extra day of Visualization and deep thinking would reap rewards every time.

If our leaders do not understand the importance of Visualization and do not allow time for "slow" thinking in the decision-making process, maybe we should teach them how to think like a leader with The Great Discovery model like the other 95%.

Chapter 12
The Big Picture

In this chapter, we are going to step back and look at the big picture. Recall our new definition of Six Sigma:

> Six Sigma is a powerful, extraordinary, proactive way of thinking that combines with a series of "Big Ideas," leading to the satisfaction of values in any situation (business and personal) – Six Sigma is Leadership in your business and personal life.

The powerful, extraordinary, proactive way of thinking is The Breakthrough Strategy: The Six Sigma Way of Thinking. We have described two current state models for the Breakthrough Strategy: The Great Discovery, which is designed to teach *Anybody* to think like a leader, and the commercial ICOV model of RDMAICSI, which is synonymous with Leadership and is designed for people who have more tools.

We mentioned the importance of Visualization and deep thinking to The Six Sigma Way of Thinking. We noted that Mikel's inclusion of Visualization in The Great Discovery, in the form of Do the Dreaming and Dream the Doing, was a breakthrough in Mikel's thinking. Visualization and deep thinking were the hidden components needed to answer Nasser's statement to Mikel, "If you could just teach us how you think." While we did not add a formal Visualization stage to the ICOV model, we noted leaders should use Visualization and deep thinking in all phases of the Breakthrough Strategy and should allow time in the process for others to use Visualization and deep thinking in decision making.

The ICOV model of RDMAICSI and The Great Discovery comparison from Figure 16 is duplicated below for convenience. While the individual steps of the ICOV Model of RDMAICSI and those of The Great Discovery comprise two separate models, they are from the exact same mold of Innovation, Execution, and Validation. Both are described as The Breakthrough Strategy. Both can be considered as The Six Sigma Way of Thinking. Both will lead to breakthrough results that satisfy values in any situation both in business and in our personal life.

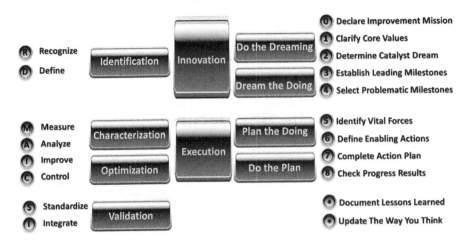

Figure 16 Comparing ICOV and The Great Discovery

We have yet to answer completely, "What is Six Sigma?" But we have answered the question, "What is The Six Sigma Way of Thinking. It is both the ICOV model of RDMAICSI and the model from The Great Discovery, the former using technical terms and the latter using lay terms.

Recall that Drucker said, "Leaders cannot be created." We have shown clearly that The Six Sigma Way of Thinking is the pathway to the creation and development of leaders at all levels of the organization and the pathway to leadership thinking in your personal life.

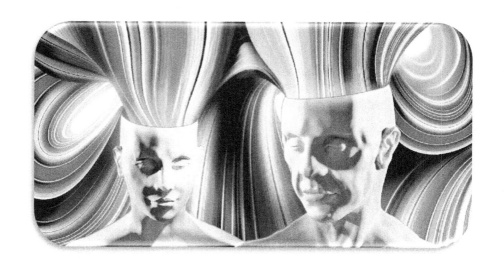

Big Ideas

Opening the Path
to
Bigger Thinking

Chapter 13
Introduction to Big Ideas

This section of the book is about "Big Ideas." Big Ideas are more abstract than the models (recipes) provided in the first section of the book for The Breakthrough Strategy. Big Ideas are concepts that you must rationalize and apply as second nature in the decision-making process. Big Ideas will help you to think deeper, be more inquisitive, and ask more questions. Comprehending this section of the book will advance your Leadership skills and change your way of thinking.

In his MindPro Lean Six Sigma training, Mikel says about Big Ideas:

> You know Bob Galvin once told me of the importance of ideas. He even wrote a book on it *The Idea of Ideas*.[25] Ideas are the stuff that brings about and highlights the will in the people. Ideas can drive the universe, and without ideas, progress isn't going to happen. Ideas need to be compelling. They need to be big ideas that can drive quantum change.

Mikel credited Big Ideas as being "the basis for transitioning Six Sigma from a toolset to a mindset." Big Ideas serve as a transform function, meaning Big Ideas are both a way to move from tools to a mindset in a strategic way, and a means to move from a mindset to the proper selection of tools during tactical implementation. Mikel liked to say, asking the right question will lead us to the right answer. In this context, if we use The Six Sigma Way of Thinking, the Big Ideas will lead us to the appropriate toolset, which in turn will lead us back to the solutions we are seeking. In short, the collection of Big Ideas is the transfer function that enables the achievement of goals and objectives.

We learned that Six Sigma is based upon three primary concepts: 1) Variation Reduction; 2) The Breakthrough Strategy; and 3) Project-by-Project Implementation. Each of these concepts is a "Big Idea" in its own right.

Bill Smith's discovery that process variation increases (processes deteriorate) over time due to shifts and drifts led him to double the design band from the traditional plus or minus three (3) short-term standard deviations to plus or minus six (6) short-term standard deviations in order to be robust to defects. Although Smith's focus was on the design of new products, as Six Sigma evolved, his concept, combined with Taguchi's thinking, evolved into the Big Idea: "Variation is Bad," and we should do everything we can to reduce variation in everything we do.

The concept of Project-by-Project Implementation or Determining a Catalyst Dream, as it is stated in The Great Discovery model, is a Big Idea that encourages focus on what is most important to us.

The thought process Mikel developed starting with The Logic Filters and ending with the current state Six Sigma Way of Thinking consisting of the commercial ICOV Model of RDMAICSI and the personal model of The Great Discovery is a Big Idea which provides a very specific pathway to changing the way we think, moving us from ordinary thinking to extraordinary thinking.

We defined Six Sigma as:

> Six Sigma is a powerful, extraordinary, proactive way of thinking that combines with a series of "Big Ideas," leading to the satisfaction of values in any situation (business and personal) – Six Sigma is Leadership in your business and personal life.

Our definition of Six Sigma has two components: 1) a way of thinking and 2) a series of Big Ideas. We discussed the "powerful, extraordinary, proactive way of thinking," The Breakthrough Strategy: The Six Sigma Way of Thinking, in the first section of the book. In this section we will learn about the Big Ideas that combine with The Breakthrough Strategy to drive, as Bob Galvin called it, quantum change in the satisfaction of values.

While working on The Great Discovery, Mikel put together a team of Six Sigma experts to help him identify the Big Ideas of Six Sigma. The team identified one hundred "Big Ideas" which they categorized and molded into what Mikel called the Ten Supreme Laws of Six Sigma: Vision, Position, Causation, Leverage, Velocity, Power, Complexity, Uncertainty, Measurement, and Constancy.

Another source of Big Ideas within Mikel's work is the ICRAtic Value Creation Strategy (Figure 8)which is duplicated below for convenience). Mikel notes in the *Fieldbook* that the Big Ideas of Six Sigma identified in the ICRAtic Value Creation Strategy form a map of issues that a Six Sigma Leader should consider in effectively executing their work. "The Big Ideas are the portals to better thinking and therefore better application, and better value realization." Mikel goes on to say, "that only by stringing the Big Ideas together does a leader begin to see the underlying code of success." So, while The Six Sigma Way of

Thinking provides a specific pathway to changing the way we think, Big Ideas provide a portal for expanded thinking that can be employed not only as we progress along the pathway but also as we work our way through each step of the pathway.

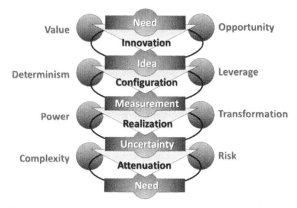

Figure 8 The ICRAtic Value Creation Strategy

Let's look at how the Ten Supreme Laws of Six Sigma and the ICRAtic Value Creation Strategy combine to provide the sixteen (16) Big Ideas (Figure 18), which we will discuss individually in the upcoming chapters.

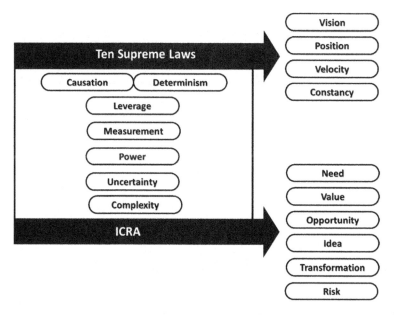

Figure 18 Current State Model "Big Ideas"

Big Ideas represent a form of mental activity that takes place to provide better awareness during our thought process as we strive for breakthrough improvement toward Value Entitlement. Big Ideas are not like a toolkit where we choose one tool over another, i.e., a screwdriver versus a hammer. Rather Big Ideas are mental activities that work together and interact to combine with The Six Sigma Way of Thinking pathway. Big Ideas combine to become a checklist of things we should consider in order to enhance the discovery process.

Each of the Big Ideas should be employed for every innovative thought and every decision. For each Big Idea not used in the thought process, the opportunity for non-optimized thought is increased. To think like a leader, all of these Big Ideas need to be practiced and refined until they become second nature.

In the coming chapters we will look at each of the sixteen (16) Big Ideas that derive from the Ten Supreme Laws and the ICRAtic Value Creation Strategy. As Mikel says, "We will look at how they integrate, operate, and light up our mind so-to-speak."

Only innovative mental structures and mindsets through big ideas provide the capability and capacity to generate future leaders.

Chapter 14
The Big Idea of Idea

The Ten Supreme Laws and the ICRAtic Value Creation Strategy combine to identify sixteen (16) Big Ideas. When selecting which of those sixteen (16) Big Ideas to discuss first, the Big Idea of Idea seems like a natural place to start.

In Robert W. Galvin's book *The Idea of Ideas,*[25] he notes two books that "immensely shaped his approach to most situations, problems, and opportunities:" Alex Osborn's book *Your Creative Power: How To Use Imagination*[26] and Bernard Baruch's book *Baruch: My Own Story.*[27] Galvin's takeaway from Alex Osborn's book was that he "described the unworthy obvious: most of us leap to conclusions, turn off ideas of others and are rebuffed too often as we offer our ideas." Galvin's takeaway from Baruch's book was "dare to go a different way, think differently."

The Big Idea of Idea starts with daring to think differently. The Six Sigma Way of Thinking: The Breakthrough Strategy provides a framework, a detailed recipe for "thinking differently." However, for The Six Sigma Way of Thinking to work, we must be open to the Big Idea of Ideas and create an environment where we "don't leap to conclusions;" "don't turn off ideas of others;" "don't rebuff ideas of others." It really isn't that complex. These are the essential rules for Brainstorming which is one of the most well-known methods of generating ideas.

As we noted previously, the ICRAtic Value Creation Strategy was developed as part of Generation III Six Sigma at DuPont with a focus on creating value. To understand how Mikel viewed The Big Idea of Idea, we must look at the ICRAtic Value Creation Strategy[4] which will be discussed in detail in the last section of this book. At this point, we will provide only enough detail to understand how the Big Idea of Idea fits into the ICRAtic Value Creation Strategy. Specifically, we want to look at the first two phases: Innovation and Configuration (Figure 19).

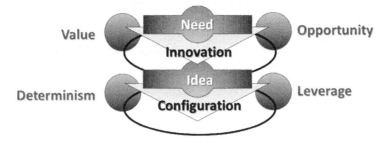

Figure 19 The Big Idea of Idea in the ICRAtic Value Creation Strategy

The Innovation phase consists of identifying a need by declaring a deprived state, or by identifying a gap between the entitlement state and the current state of value, resulting in initiation of a search for favorable conditions which provide an opportunity to optimize the need.

Google Dictionary[28] defines "Idea" as a thought or suggestion as to a possible course of action. The result of the Innovation phase is an idea, a conceptual model, that has the opportunity to increase value if appropriate action is taken.

While the Innovation phase of the ICRAtic Value Creation Strategy is driven by Need, the Configuration phase is driven by Ideas. The Configuration phase refines the conceptual model by designing a pattern of determinism or causation that exploits or leverages those ideas.

It took me many years to understand the ICRAtic Value Creation Strategy which is why the last part of this book will discuss the ICRAtic Value Creation Strategy in its own section. For now, let's step back and take a macro view:

> A Value Need drives Innovation, resulting in Ideas that can be implemented to reduce the need, which in turn will then increase value. At this point, the Ideas are in a conceptual state. The Ideas are then refined in the Configuration phase by determining a chain of causation and evaluating their leverage.

Whether ideas come from uncovering the vital few conditions from the existing or known variable or they come from new or unknown ideas revealed from innovation, **Ideas are what allow reduction of needs to be realized.**

Chapter 15
Vision: Beyond Status Quo

In our discussion on Ideas, we talked about daring to think differently, encouraging the flow of ideas, using a value-driven approach, and the importance of ideas to the ICRAtic Value Creation Strategy. We will now look at the Big Idea of Vision.

There are many definitions of Vision, but I like this definition: Vision is the act or power of imagination,[13] as compared to the definition of Idea: a thought or suggestion as to a possible course of action.

John Maynard Keynes' book, *The General Theory of Employment, Interest and Money*,[29] written in 1936, has the following quote in the preface:

> "The difficulty lies, not in the new ideas, but in escaping from the old ones, which ramify, for those brought up as most of us have been, into every corner of our minds."

Vision is the ability to see, imagine, the strategic ramifications of beneficial change, and it is the ability to escape from the old, the status quo, that lurks in the corner of our minds and drives us to resist change. Ideas are the result of Vision. Ideas are the tactical means of creating beneficial change, while Vision is the identification of the strategic thing that we seek to change. Both Vision and Ideas rely on creative imagination, but Vision is not possible without imagination.

Vision is forward-looking for positive change, whereas Ideas relate to the status quo in addressing both positive and negative problems. This view applies to our individual lives as well. Satisfaction in our personal life is achieved as we move ever closer to the fulfillment of our values. The more we can understand and define our values, the easier it will be to think about a beneficial future outcome toward reaching the entitlement of those values.

Imagination is defined as: "The act or power of forming a mental image of something not present to the senses or never before wholly perceived in reality; a creative ability; ability to confront and deal with a problem; the thinking or active mind."[13] Imagination is what separates Leaders from Doers. Not just the ability, but the willingness to "dare to go a different way, think differently," as Baruch said.

Some change management practitioners have equated change as being synonymous with Leadership, noting that if there is no positive change, there is only status quo or worse. Mikel's philosophy of Vision is consistent with this thought. However, Mikel would say, Leadership is the ability to visualize Breakthrough Change, which is measurable. Recognize in the ICOV model of RDMAICSI and Do the Dreaming in The Great Discovery model are about Vision, seeking beneficial change, thinking differently. Thinking not just about change but Breakthrough Change, change where there are no constraints. Mikel noted that success is driven by the ability of Leaders to determine their values and to visualize how they can reach an entitlement state. He says Vision by Leaders "gives employees the freedom to explore new ideas and concepts and the power and resources to make decisions and implement breakthrough change."

Interestingly, Vision is one of the Ten Supreme Laws but is not specifically included as a Big Idea in the ICRAtic Value Creation Strategy. The first portion of the model (Figure 19) is repeated below for convenience.

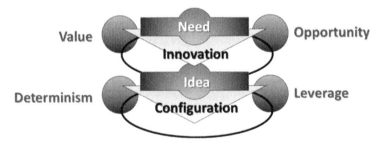

Figure 19 The Big Idea of Idea in the ICRAtic Value Creation Strategy

Innovation is the introduction of something new; a new idea, method, or device. Innovation is the outcome of an active imagination, an outcome of our ability to visualize how to satisfy our needs and move us closer to Value Entitlement. While vision is not explicitly identified in the ICRAtic Value Creation Strategy, it is the foundation of the model.

The last section of this book is dedicated to the ICRAtic Value Creation Strategy. We will not get into the details of how to improve our vision in this chapter. At this point, it is simply important that Vision is the foundational Big Idea that takes us beyond status quo and moves us from ordinary thinking to extraordinary thinking.

As a college professor, I liked to end the last class for my seniors with a poem written by Sam Walter Foss in the late 1800's called "The Calf-Path."

Breaking away from the Calf-Path of the Mind requires Vision, which is the bedrock of The Breakthrough Strategy. I shared this poem as my senior students and I parted, hoping they'd understand that what they'd learned in college was simply information. It was up to them to fight the Calf-Path of the Mind, the culture of holding on to the status quo which is prevalent in the world they were about to enter. If they didn't fight back, they would soon be infected with the disease of the Calf-Path of the Mind.

The Calf-Path

Sam Walter Foss

One day through the primeval wood,
a calf walked home as good calves should;
But made a trail all bent askew,
a crooked trail as all calves do.
Since then three hundred years have fled,
and I infer the calf is dead.
But still he left behind his trail,
and thereby hangs my moral tale.

The trail was taken up next day,
by a lone dog that passed that way;
And then a wise bellwether sheep,
pursued the trail o'er vale and steep,
And drew the flock behind him, too,
as good bellwethers always do.
And from that day, o'er hill and glade,
through those old woods, a path was made.

And many men wound in and out,
and dodged and turned and bent about,
And uttered words of righteous wrath,
because 'twas such a crooked path;
But still they followed --- do not laugh ---
the first migrations of that calf.
And through this winding wood-way stalked,
because he wobbled when he walked.

This forest path became a lane,
that bent and turned and turned again;
This crooked lane became a road,
where many a poor horse with his load,
Toiled on beneath the burning sun,
 and traveled some three miles in one.
And thus a century and a half,
they trod the footsteps of that calf.

The years passed on in swiftness fleet,
the road became a village street;
And this, before men were aware,
a city's crowded thoroughfare.
And soon the central street was this,
of a renowned metropolis;
And men two centuries and a half,
trod in the footsteps of that calf.

Each day a hundred thousand men,
follow this zigzag calf again,
And o'er his crooked journey went,
the traffic of a continent.
A hundred thousand men were led,
by one calf near three centuries dead.
They followed still his crooked way,
and lost one hundred years a day;
For thus such reverence is lent,
to a well-established precedent.

A moral lesson this might teach,
were I ordained and called to preach;
For men are prone to go it blind,
along the calf-path of the mind,
And work away from sun to sun,
to do what other men have done.
They follow in the beaten track,
and in and out, and forth and back,
And still their devious course pursue,
to keep the path that others do.

They keep the path a sacred groove,
along which all their lives they move;
But how the old wood-gods laugh,
who first saw that primeval calf.
Ah, many things this tale might teach ---
but I am not ordained to preach.

Effect is a function of a cause. The key principle is to focus on the problem not the symptom.

Chapter 16
Determinism and the BOPI Structure

Determinism is one of the sixteen Big Ideas and appears in both the Ten Supreme Laws and the ICRAtic Value Creation Strategy. Mikel most often refers to Determinism as deterministic reasoning or causation. Determinism is a way of thinking and is critical to The Six Sigma Way of Thinking, just as the processes Visualization and Deep Thinking.

In equation form, Determinism is Y is equal to a function of X, written $Y = f(X)$. Simply stated, Determinism is the idea that the effect is a function of a cause or more than one cause. Since everything has a cause, the fundamental principle is to focus on those causes which represent the problem, the X's, as opposed to focusing on the symptom, the Y. Conversely, improving the cause will improve the effect. Another way to say this is the outcome (output) is a function of the inputs, so by improving the inputs, the outcome improves.

$$Y = f(X)$$
$$Effect = f(Cause)$$
$$Output = f(Input)$$

Figure 20 Determinism

Understanding the concept of determinism is often a paradigm shift for many leaders. The effect is most commonly the primary focus of discussion; but, to be effective, leaders should spend most of their time focusing on the cause. Once leaders understand that breakthrough results are achieved when focusing on the X's instead of Y's, their whole way of thinking changes, and they will be able to quickly identify what we call "Y-side Thinkers" versus "X-side Thinkers."

In addition to the three primary ways shown in Figure 20, Determinism can be expressed many other ways:

- Symptoms are a function of problems.
- Value satisfaction is a function of our behavior.
- Products are a function of the process.
- Answers are a function of questions.
- Yield is a function of defects.

From a business perspective, Determinism is represented by the BOPI structure.

What happens at the business level of the organization is a function of what happens at the organization level which is a function of what happens at the process level which is a function of what happens at the individual level. This example of determinism is called The BOPI Structure.

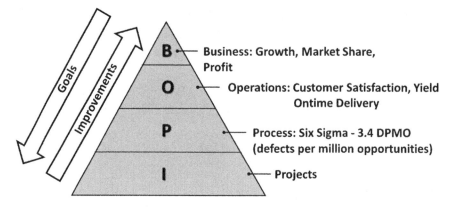

Figure 21 BOPI Structure

Strategic goals are created at the Business level and cascade down to Operation goals, which cascade down to Process goals and lead to projects at the Individual level. Improvements resulting from projects flow back up through the organization to improve the process goals, operation goals, and strategic business goals.

When we understand there is a perpetual chain of Causation, we can change what we monitor and what we control. We should monitor the Y, the effect, the symptom, the product, the yield, or even our values. Monitoring the Y, tells us when something is not going as planned. But we control X's: The causes, the problems, the processes, the defects, our behaviors. When we control the optimal settings for the "knobs and dials" of the X's, we will achieve the resulting Y we desire.

Determinism is also an integral part of the personal model for Six Sigma: The Great Discovery (Figure 22). As we discussed previously, the driving force behind any Breakthrough Mission is a need to satisfy our values. Stated in the form of determinism, the satisfaction of our values is a function of the need gaps: Satisfaction of our Values = f (Need Gaps). Reduction of these need gaps aggregate to form our Mission, which is Value Entitlement.

The Catalyst in The Great Discovery model represents the Project we have chosen to reduce the vital few need gaps. The use of the word Catalyst and the way Mikel placed it into The Great Discovery Diagram often causes some confusion. As we noted, Catalyst represents the project upon which we have chosen to focus in order to reduce the need gaps, which then will increase one or more of our values. However, in The Great Discovery model, Catalyst also represents the last milestone in the project and the point at which we achieve mission success. Mikel used Catalyst, the project of focus, the final milestone, and mission success interchangeably.

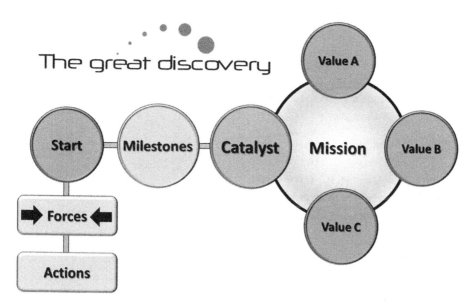

Figure 22 Determinism in The Great Discovery

The Catalyst is the project which has the most leverage in reducing the need gaps on which we are going to focus. Stated in deterministic form, reduction of

Need is a function of the Catalyst on which we choose to focus: Reduction of Need = f(Catalyst).

Like the BOPI Structure used in organizations, the personal model of The Great Discovery relies on a deterministic structure throughout. The following is noted in The Great Discovery Training:

> Accomplishing the Catalyst, completing the project, is a function of achieving the milestones which lead us from the start to the Catalyst. The start is represented by the first milestone of the project. The Catalyst represents not only the project itself but also the last milestone of the project, project completion: Catalyst = f (Milestones).

> In order to start the project, first milestone, we analyze the driving and restraining forces that are inhibiting action: Milestones = f (Forces).

> When we create an imbalance in the forces, we are ready to take action: Action = f (Imbalance in Forces).

> Once the process of analyzing forces and taking action is complete, we are ready to move to the next milestone: The next milestone = f (the preceding milestone).

> We continue until we have achieved the Catalyst, reached the last milestone, and mission success.

Earlier, we noted that answers are a function of questions. Applying the concept of determinism, we should focus on the questions, not on the answer. Mikel liked to use this example:

> How many times have we seen it, where somebody asked the wrong question? Everybody goes off, then comes back with the right answer, to the wrong question. I would much rather have the wrong answer to the right question. I can at least get the correct answer eventually. But if I hold on to the wrong question, I always pursue the inappropriate answer.

I like to take agendas and minutes from important meetings. Almost always, the focus is on the symptom, the Y, rather than problems, which might be causing the symptom. We need to increase market share, sales, profits, etc. We have too many defects. These are all symptoms. Once, the symptom is introduced, there is no value in continuing to discuss it. The meeting should turn to the problems, in order to identify the vital few causes of the negative effect.

A tool we use to identify the causes of a problem is called a fishbone diagram, given its name for its skeletal framework. The fishbone diagram, also known as an Ishikawa Diagram, is named after its creator, Kaoru Ishikawa.[30] It's also referred to as a Cause and Effect chart where causes are the X's, and the effect, the symptom, is the Y. The fishbone diagram is simply an outline with the symptom as the header, main ideas extended off the backbone, and sub-ideas extending off main ideas (Figure 23) The fishbone diagram is often used as part of brainstorming sessions to organize ideas.

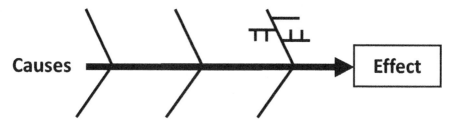

Figure 23 Fishbone Diagram

Another method often used to organize ideas while brainstorming is called an affinity diagram, or K-J method after its creator Jiro Kawakita. This method is sometimes referred to as Space Saturate and Group. Ideas are typically written on sticky notes and used to saturate a space. The ideas are then organized into homogeneous groups and given a heading. The groups are then organized into a process.

Whether by using a fishbone diagram or an affinity diagram, or an actual outline, the focus of the meeting should be on the causes of the effects after a short introduction of the symptom itself.

While you may not have heard of deterministic reasoning or have not seen the $Y = f(X)$ equation, you might have heard about root cause analysis. Root cause analysis is the application of determinism to find the root cause, the root X, contributing to the effect, the Y, the symptom, we are seeing or feeling. A commonly used technique taught when teaching root cause analysis is called "The 5 Whys." Once you have defined the effect on which you want to focus, you ask "Why?" By asking why, you are seeking the cause. Then you ask "Why?" four more times. You are driving down the chain of causation, using deterministic reasoning, searching for the root cause.

As noted, deterministic reasoning, or simply Determinism, is as much of The Breakthrough Strategy: The Six Sigma Way of Thinking as is Visualization and Deep Thinking. Those who do not apply deterministic reasoning as a primary thinking skill are depriving themselves of a critical aspect of Leadership thinking.

Chapter 17
Value: the "Big Y"

It should be clear that Value is a Big Idea. The ICOV model of RDMAICSI focuses on Value Entitlement between the customer and the provider (business) as the driving need for change. In Mikel's words, the focus of Generation III Six Sigma at DuPont was "on growth, under the concept that the customer and the provider realize Value in every critical aspect of the business relationship." In The Great Discovery model, "Clarify Core Values" is step number one.

From the previous chapter, we noted Determinism in equation form is $Y = f(X)$. Mikel calls value creation, the "Big Y." The function (f) is The Breakthrough Strategy, which is applied to Six Sigma projects, X's, or in the case of The Great Discovery, the Catalyst Dream.

Google Dictionary provides two definitions for Value when used as a noun:

1) the regard that something is held to deserve; the importance, worth, or usefulness of something; and

2) a person's principles or standards of behavior; one's judgment of what's important in life.

The first definition of value is more of an organizational definition which befits the ICOV model of RDMAICSI, while the second definition describes value from a personal perspective and befits The Great Discovery.

Regardless of the perspective of the definition, values are those things important to us and are at the center of the way we think. Dissatisfaction with values creates a driving need for change from the current state to an entitlement state.

Mikel categorized Value by dissecting it into chart form with three broad categories: Utility, Availability (Access), and Worth (Figure 24):

Value	Utility	Form Fit Function
	Availability (Access)	Volume Location Timing
	Worth	Intellectual Emotional Economic

Figure 24 Dr. Mikel J. Harry's Categorization of Value

- Utility breaks down into form, fit, and function, or how beneficial or useful something is to us. The more utility, the more satisfied we are and thus the more value we receive. It is also important to note that Utility as described by form, fit, and function is a classic means of describing quality.

- Availability is dissected into Volume, Location, and Timing. Something may have potential value, but if we cannot access it in the right volume when we need it, or if we must exert more effort to achieve availability, then value is diminished. Having parts at the "right volume, right location, and right time" was a phase commonly used in lean manufacturing.

- Worth, while somewhat synonymous with value, was considered by Mikel to be a measurement of value and he developed three scales to measure the value we feel: intellectual, emotional, and economic.

While economic worth is obvious, intellectual and emotional worth are less so. Intellectual stimulation is what challenges and motivates us to be engaged and creative. Intellectual worth leads to higher levels of satisfaction and effectiveness. Emotional worth has two critical elements: personal impact and clarity. Personal impact occurs only when we internalize and think about both the positive and negative consequences of not changing. Clarity occurs only when we make the connection between our current state and our entitlement state and realize action can create a breakthrough change. This is why The Breakthrough Strategy: The Six Sigma Way of Thinking – Leadership must focus on values and the need gap as a foundation for change.

Mikel's chart doesn't clearly express his full philosophy of value. He believed that Worth was a measure of how much value that Utility and Availability provided. He also believed that both Utility and Availability had to exist concurrently in order to have value in the form of both quality (form, fit, and function) and availability (right volume, right location, and right time).

When Mikel created The Great Discovery, he replaced Availability (Access) with the word Importance. It is not clear from Mikel's writings why he made this change and quite frankly it is difficult to rationalize given Mikel's view that Utility and Availability (access) had to exist concurrently for value to exist. When asked about why Mikel may have changed Access to Importance, Cathy Lawson, co-author of *The Great Discovery*, replied:

> I think the other 95% can relate to values of something of "importance" to them. He (Mikel) would say your values drive your behaviors and your decisions. I believe that the word "importance" was brought in to emphasize that concept to the individual.

Sandra Harry, Chairman of the Board of Dr. Mikel J. Harry's Six Sigma Management Institute and an expert on The Great Discovery in her own right, confirmed Cathy's thoughts:

> Mikel was dedicated to getting The Great Discovery to a point everyone could understand. He spent the whole summer with a friend who he was mentoring and who was not familiar with Six Sigma. They worked on it until the friend understood it. It seems clear that the change from Availability to Importance was a way to communicate the concept of value in lay terms.

We noted form, fit, and function (Utility) reflect Value from a "quality" perspective and that Mikel changed Availability to Importance in The Great Discovery. Since Mikel believed that Utility and Availability had to exist concurrently for Value to exist, it is consistent to combine and label them "things of importance," allowing us to simplify Mikel's Categorization of Value chart into a definition.

Value is something of importance, measured along intellectual, emotional, and economic scales of Worth.

When looking at the intersection between the customer and the provider, which is Value, the customer desires form, fit, and function at a reasonable cost, while the provider wants to optimize their capability and capacity at a profitable cost.

Mikel liked to put things into equation form. For Value, he used the equation:

$$\text{Customer Value} = \frac{\textbf{Form x Fit x Function}}{\textbf{Cost}}$$

$$\text{Provider Value} = \frac{\textbf{Capability x Capacity}}{\textbf{Cost}}$$

$$\text{Personal Value} = \frac{\textbf{The Things Important To Us}}{\textbf{Cost}}$$

Cost is not only dollars, but the time, effort, and opportunity loss in order to achieve the things important to us.

Mikel defined Value Entitlement as a "rightful level of expectation," in other words, the state in which our values are fully satisfied. When our values are not satisfied, we feel dissatisfaction and a need for change. In this sense, our values, whether on an organizational level or on a personal level, are what drive us to seek breakthrough change.

Leadership brings clarity and cuts through the fog of ambiguity by providing vision and direction. Mikel's leadership models of ICOV and The Great Discovery provide a path for determining core values, defining the need gaps for each value by comparing the entitlement state to the current state, and providing a method of accomplishing a breakthrough in closing the need gaps.

Mikel frequently stated, "There's two ways we can go. We can wait for opportunity to happen, or we can design our own destiny." Waiting is reactive, and designing our own way is proactive. Leadership is proactive. This is why both the ICOV model of RDMAICSI and The Great Discovery start with the philosophy that Value is the driving force behind change.

Data is not information: they must be analytically tortured to confess its meaning.

Chapter 18
The Relationship Between
Value, Need, and Change

In this chapter, we will expand our discussion on the Big Idea of Value and how it relates to the Big Idea of Need. We previously noted that the driving force behind any breakthrough is a need to satisfy our values, where the need is the gap between what ought to be (entitlement), and what is (the current state). We also noted, **"Value is something of importance, measured along intellectual, emotional, and economic scales of Worth."**

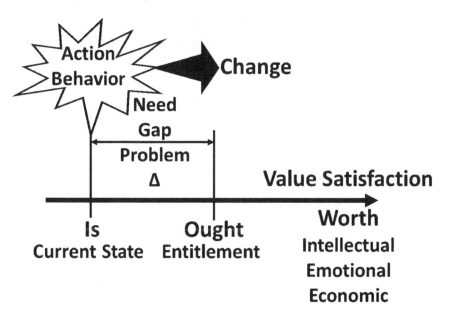

Figure 25 Value - Need - Change

Need is defined as a lack of something requisite, desirable, or useful, a condition requiring supply or relief.[13] We recognize there is a problem that needs to be addressed when the gap between the current state and our entitlement state is large enough that relief is needed. When we take action to bridge that gap, the result is change. So, the satisfaction of our values requires us to take action toward breakthrough change from the current state of value satisfaction toward the entitlement state of value satisfaction along the scales of intellectual, emotional, and economic worth.

As discussed previously, the intersection of the customer's values and the provider's values in the commercial model is Value Entitlement, the business relationship, or simply business. Mikel developed a second interpretation of this model that he called the Need-Do interaction where the customer has the Need, and the provider has the Do. This model is the basis of Six Sigma's focus on the customer.

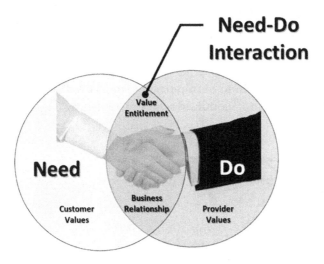

Figure 26 Need-Do Interaction

Even in the personal model, the Need-Do interaction is applicable in that the interaction is where value occurs. The Need must be strong enough for us to recognize. From the Do side, our actions must be focused on the need to the point that they leverage reduction of the need in such a way that we create breakthrough results toward Value Entitlement. As we close the gap, we make a profound intervention and move toward satisfaction of our values.

It is important to understand the difference between Value and Need. In the determinism model of $Y = f(X)$, Value = f(Need), Value = f(Problems). Value is what we want to satisfy (the effect), and Need is the gap between our current state and our entitlement state that will satisfy our Values.

Abraham Maslow's Hierarchy of Needs was published in 1943 in an article called "A Theory of Human Motivation."[31] Maslow's original "needs" were physiological, safety, love/belonging, esteem, and self-actualization, although the words describing these "needs" have changed over time. While Maslow called these human motivators "needs," in our language, we would say that "needs or motivators," as defined by Maslow, are actually "values."

For example, we would view what Maslow classifies as a physiological need, as a "value" of physiological satisfaction. We would then categorize the physiological needs that were not being satisfied and identify vital few gaps that are the cause of the dissatisfaction. The point being made is that Value and Need are not synonymous. Values are effects (Y's), and Needs are causes (X's, problems, gaps). We are not going to get into the middle of the intellectual fight, but some would argue that Maslow's hierarchy of needs has been debunked. You are encouraged to do your own research.

Kurt Lewin is known as one of the pioneers of social, organizational, and applied psychology. In his 1936 publication *Principles of Topological Psychology*,[32] Lewin presented the equation, $B = f(P, E)$, where Behavior is a function of the Person and their Environment. The Person represents a person's intrinsic traits or personality, and the Environment represents external factors. Lewin saw motivation as an interaction of a specific person in a particular situation, and he believed the environment had more influence than the intrinsic characteristics of the person.

Lewin noted that historically, situation and environment were used synonymously, but he wanted to distinguish between the two. From a lay perspective, situation is used to describe a single event at a moment in time where all variables are known and unique to each person. Environment, on the other hand, represented a possible event where there are variables that are not known, including the person, and thus prediction is required.

As we noted previously, how we act and what we do is a result of the lacking satisfaction in our values, Value Satisfaction = f(Behavior), which is a two-way relationship. We can also say Behavior is a function of our Values, $B = f(Values)$. How we act is a function of what we believe and our need for value satisfaction. This equation is consistent with Lewin's equation, $B = f(P, E)$.

Our values are individual and affected by the situation or the environment. Whether they are personal or corporate, values influence our behavior, and our behavior or actions influence value satisfaction. The words behavior and action can be considered to be synonymous.

On the subject of value and behavior, Mikel noted:

> Significant emotional events take place when it becomes apparent that old practices no longer satisfy, and the path is cleared for new beliefs and values to be introduced and accepted. There is a direct correlation between behavior change and the consequences of not changing.

Also, from the deterministic reasoning perspective, behavior will result from the satisfaction gap of values. In other words, behavior is how we act and what we do when our values are not fully satisfied.

In any organization, values should be reflected in the actions the organization measures and rewards. Since organization values drive what people think is or is not essential within an organization, people need to see how their values drive behavior, and how those values impact their individual jobs and ultimately the organization. Business measurements drive values. Values drive how people work. How people work determines profitability.

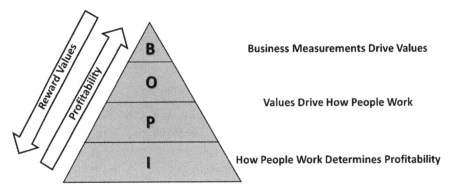

Figure 27 Rewarded Values Drive Profitability

Actions and contributions should be traceable back to core values. Unfortunately, too often organizations do not clearly define their values and then wonder why their reward system does not work.

In *The Blue Book*, Mikel describes B.F. Skinner's Superstitious Dance, operant conditioning:

> Pigeons were placed in a box with a feeding mechanism that randomly delivered food pellets regardless of how the pigeons behaved. The pigeons, however, began to correlate certain activities with receiving food. For instance, if a pigeon raised its wing and food appeared, it would correlate raising its wing with being fed. However, if the pigeon began pecking its beak against a wall or scratching its foot when

another pellet appeared, it might modify its behavior to re-create the most recent action that delivered food. While behavior that is rewarded tends to be strengthened, often the behavior that occurs immediately prior to the reinforcement is coincidental.

Humans are not pigeons. However, from Skinner's experiment, we can learn about the importance of designing a value system. The reward system must be clear and unambiguous so that we do not reward coincidental acts. Skinner's experiment also shows empirically that if we clearly define our values and design a value system only around rewards that we value, we will change not only our own personal behavior but the behavior of the organization.

As noted previously, Mikel came to understand that the driving force behind any breakthrough is a need to satisfy our values, where need is defined as the gap between Value Entitlement—full satisfaction—and our current state of value satisfaction (Figure 7, repeated below for convenience). Value is increased, moved closer to entitlement, by closing the "need gap."

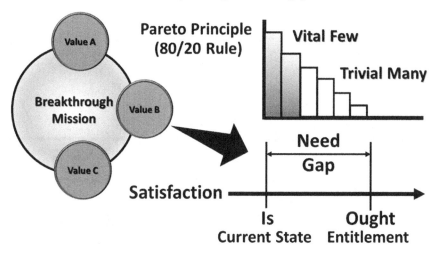

Figure 7 Need

In the Six Sigma Way of Thinking, we Recognize we have a problem, a need. We apply DMAIC: Define, Measure, Analyze, Improve, Control to the problem to achieve an improved state. Then we Standardize and Integrate the problem into our culture in a way that affects future behavior. The same process exists in The Great Discovery, although we use different terms to describe the process. The Six Sigma Way of Thinking is the "function" that takes us through the chain of causation.

Values = f (Needs) ➜ Needs = f(Behavior) ➜ Behavior = f(Change)

Our values drive our Needs

Our Needs drive our Behavior

Our Behavior drives change

Change modifies our Behavior

Behavior reduces our Needs

Reduction in our Needs satisfies our Values

Chapter 19
Finding Opportunity

Opportunity is one of the twelve Big Ideas in the ICRAtic Value Creation Strategy, but those familiar with Six Sigma will also recognize Opportunity as it exists as a measure of value in the conversion of defects to a Sigma value, i.e., Six Sigma is 3.4 Defects per Million Opportunities.

Mikel defined Opportunity as "a set of conditions favorable to some end." When looking at defects per million opportunities, "Defect" is often used with opportunity to form "Defect Opportunity," which is a set of conditions favorable to a nonconformance to standard. In the case of a Defect Opportunity, the end is negative, but the statement could have also been made in the positive form, i.e., a set of conditions favorable to yield or a set of conditions favorable to conformance to standard or favorable to a good product. Sigma, as in Six Sigma, only applies at the Opportunity level.

The cycle of Value Creation, ICRA, which will be discussed in more detail in the last section of this book, is briefly described as follows. Innovation is based on a need, which is a gap between an entitlement state and a current state, with respect to something of value. We then look for Opportunities to generate ideas for meeting that need. These ideas are then measured and tested in an idealized model of Value Creation. Then we look for Opportunity to Configure and Realize the envisioned value proposition. Finally, we Attenuate the gaps. In other words, when conditions are favorable to the creation of value, i.e., properly identified and aligned, we have an Opportunity to create value which satisfies the need and relieves the deprived state.

Opportunity is comprised of the problematic ideas of condition and advantage. In other words, these are the causative concepts we consider when looking to produce opportunity. Therefore, an opportunity is a set of conditions configured such they have an advantage in achieving an envisioned end. Opportunity is optimized by searching for favorable conditions.

Often Opportunity becomes visible from negative day-to-day consequences. While not always recognized, Opportunity also becomes visible through improvement projects. Mikel liked to say, "Constraints are an Opportunity for Achievement." We need to recognize constraints and roadblocks as an Opportunity for improvement versus a problem that is restricting us from improvement. Mikel was a U.S. Marine and liked to talk about Leadership in military terms:

> If you're not taking flak when you're a leader, something is wrong. When you do it right, it creates a lot of debate, a lot of discussion, and for some people a lot of grief because it exposes them. It flushes out the restrainers to change and deadwood in an organization.

> You know you're over the target when you hear the sound of flak. When you're getting close to the epicenter of change, antiaircraft guns start going off. As a leader, the flak tells you that you are over the target. And it's on that battlefield, so to speak, where your role as a leader is required. So, don't avoid the flak when you hear it. Go to it, because that's an area of change and that constitutes opportunity.

The Blue Book provides comments from Bruce Miyashita, McKinsey & Company consultant, who served as Six Sigma Champion at Bombardier:

> Our challenge was to fight what Yvan Allaire, Bombardier Executive Vice President, described as the "Success Breeds Failure Syndrome." To see the need for change even when, by most indicators, things have never been better, and to see how much untapped opportunity exists if we focus our resources in the right places with the right tool, data, and know-how. This is the first hurdle—to help people see the need for and the benefits of change.

Leaders not only turn roadblocks and constraints into Opportunity but are proactive in searching for Opportunities that will create value in everything they do. It is the role of Leaders to help people see the need for and the benefits of change and to teach them how to search for Opportunities in everything they do regardless of their historical successes or failures.

Chapter 20
The Importance of Position

Earlier, we referenced Lewin's equation, B = f(P, E), Behavior is a function of the Person and the Environment, and noted that Situation is used to describe a single event at a moment in time where all variables are known and unique to each person. One of Mikel's Ten Supreme Laws was Position. Even though they are from different fields of study, Lewin's concept of Situation and Mikel's concept of Position are very similar, if not synonymous.

Lewin's work is from a field of study called Field Theory. Lewin started with the equation B = f(S), which he described as follows:

> If one represents behavior or any kind of mental event by B and the whole situation including the person by S, then B may be treated as a function of S. In this equation, the function f, or its general form [B = f(S)], represents what one ordinarily calls a law. If one substitutes for the variables in this formula, the constants which are constant for the individual case, one gets the application to the concrete situation.[32]

Lewin goes on to say, "… Galilean concepts demand that we no longer seek the 'cause' of events in the nature of a single isolated object, but in the relationship between an object and its surroundings." It was from this perspective that Lewin moved from a concrete situation of known variables to a dynamic situation, which he called "Life Space," which required prediction of the person and the environment to hypothesize the situation.

One does not need to be an expert in the field of psychology to see the similarity between Lewin's thoughts and the philosophy underlying Mikel's Breakthrough Strategy, which originated from his original Logic Filters model (Figure 6).

Let's compare Lewin's theory with the viewpoint described in Mikel's Logic Filters. The Logic Filters were based upon Mikel's desire to take "The Total Universe of All Variables" and filter them down into concrete solutions for a specific situation. The Breakthrough Strategy: The Six Sigma Way of Thinking, whether through the ICOV model of RDMAICSI or The Great Discovery, further refines this model. The objective of the Breakthrough Strategy is to define and measure the constants in the universe of unknown variables that can be leveraged to provide breakthrough results from the current state to an entitlement state through behavior (action).

Mikel, like Lewin, recognized that a given person in a given environment is likely to make different decisions than some other person in that same environment. Also, a person will make different decisions in different environments. This is the Big Idea of Position.

Position is determined through Define and Measure in the ICOV model of RDMAICSI and through the development of milestones in The Great Discovery. The factors that we need to leverage and/or the milestones we need to accomplish will be different depending on our position and our values.

Position is also relevant from an organization perspective. For example, regardless of what value is important to the organization, there is some relative position between them and their competitors. Also, each corporation has its own culture, just like each person has their own characteristics and the environment is different for each situation. From this perspective we could rewrite Lewin's equation as:

> Behavior is a function of Values, whether the values represent a person or an organization, and is a function of Position in the environment. This is now written as $B = f$ (Values, Position), replacing Person with Values and Environment with the Position within the environment.

While not explicitly identified under the label of Position, the idea of position is apparent throughout Six Sigma. In variation analysis, we typically recognize three major sources of variation:

- Positional variation where variation occurs within a piece
- Cyclical variation where variation occurs piece-to-piece
- Temporal variation when variation occurs across time

These three major sources of variation are forms of Position in the system of occurrence.

Looking at these three sources of variation from a human perspective:

- Positional variation represents our behavior for a specific situation given specific environmental conditions.

- Cyclical variation acknowledges variation, and that the same person will make different decisions under different environmental conditions.

- Temporal variation acknowledges values change, and a person may make different decisions over time.

The current position has an impact on directions to the destination, total costs and resources, total time to destination, the types of supplies needed for the journey, the kind of knowledge required, and many other things.

Positioning is an important Big Idea in implementing the Breakthrough Strategy. To paraphrase Mikel on Position as described in The Great Discovery:

Step 1: We must fully define the current position.

Step 2: We must define a clear vision of our future position, our entitlement position.

Step 3: We must measure the Need, the gap, between our entitlement position and our current position.

Step 4: We must establish checkpoints, milestones along the path that will lead us to a reduction of the gap.

"That's how you get out of the box and win."

Leverage is setting the odds in your favor to gain a distinct advantage in anything you do.

Chapter 21
Leverage Brings Breakthrough Results

Leverage in the form of mechanical advantage is attributed to Archimedes (287 – 212 B.C.), and he is often quoted as saying, "Give me a lever long enough, and a fulcrum on which to place it, and I shall move the world."

Etymology is a study of the origin of words and how their meanings have changed throughout history. Today, the word Leverage is used in several different ways:[13]

- The action of a lever or the mechanical advantage gained by it

- Figuratively as a form of power, effectiveness, or exploitation for accomplishing a purpose

- Leverage from a financial perspective where debt is used to enhance one's speculative capacity

Levers are all around us: teeter-totters, pry bars, scissors, etc. By moving the lever along the fulcrum to lengthen the effort arm in proportion to the resistance arm, it takes less effort to lift the load. From a system perspective, we can think of effort as being the input and the load being the output. Using leverage, we can get more output with less input.

A lever is a simple machine consisting of a beam (lever) which is hinged on a fulcrum to provide mechanical advantage (Figure 28).

As an example, let's think about the lever as a teeter-totter. Say both the load and the effort are represented by 150-pound people, and both the resistance arm and the effort arm are six feet from the fulcrum to their sitting position. What is the system doing? The input is equal to the output, so the system is stable. The lever is parallel to the ground, and neither person is going up or down. We call this condition steady-state.

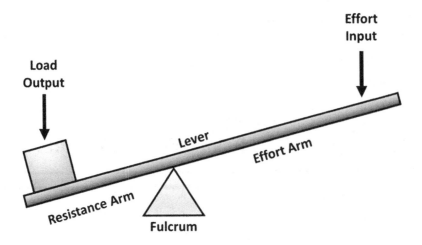

Figure 28 Lever

There are two ways to create an imbalance in the system:

1. Increase input, apply more effort on the input side. This will raise the output load and create an imbalance in the system.

2. Increase the effort arm with respect to the resistance arm by moving the lever relative to the fulcrum. If I make the distance of the effort arm eight feet and the length of the resistance arm four feet, I can increase my leverage and lift the load without increasing my effort. That's the idea of mechanical advantage or what is called leverage.

The use of leverage in a financial sense is the most modern use. Financial leverage is where debt is used to acquire additional assets hoping that the increase in asset value will be larger than the interest on the debt, thus magnifying assets with someone else's money. The financier is leveraging debt to build assets.

In The Six Sigma Way of Thinking, we use leverage figuratively as a form of power, effectiveness, or exploitation for accomplishing project success. We have used the term "leverage" several times in association with the Pareto Principle, the 80/20 Rule, which says 20% of the effort will accomplish 80% of the result and the remaining 20% of the result will require 80% of the effort. As such, leverage can be considered a state of conditional advantage where we focus on the vital few and ignore the trivial many.

Mikel notes that this is a way of saying, "Let's not make perfection the enemy of good." As noted previously, the world is dynamic, and 80% of the result may be enough to allow some other item of value to become more important.

We looked at leverage in the form of mechanical advantage using the teeter-totter example. Now let's look at leverage from an analytical advantage perspective applied to variation reduction. Let's say there are two variables, A and B, that come together to create an outcome. Using the deterministic model, this is represented by $Y = f(A, B)$. For this example, assume that variable A has one unit of variation, and variable B has sixteen units of variation. Mathematically, variations are additive. That means that the variation in Y is $16 + 1 = 17$ units of variation. If my objective is to reduce the variation in Y, I can reduce either the variation in variable A or variable B.

In this example, if we apply the Pareto principle where 20% of our effort will achieve 80% of the potential result to Variable A, we get 0.8 (1 x 80%) units of improvement. However, if we apply the Pareto principle to variable B, we would get 12.8 (16 x 80%) units of improvement. There is much more leverage toward our objective by applying our effort to variable B versus variable A. Variable B exerts a greater influence on variation reduction than variable A, so variable B is the vital few, and variable A is the trivial many.

In The Great Discovery, leverage is used in the Plan the Doing stage of Defining the Vital Few Forces and Defining Enabling Actions. In order to move from one milestone to the next, you must leverage the driving forces that will create forward momentum and at the same time disable the restraining forces that serve to hold you back. As Mikel notes, "By focusing on the Vital Few forces, we spend our time on the things that matter the most. It is about working smarter not harder. Failure to employ this step is why many people give up and why many executives run out of patience with many good ideas."

Many times, the various forces can be engaged in a way that their combined effect is more than the simple sum of the individual effects. The concept of leveraging is applying forces in such a way that their combined effect is greater together.

Peter M. Senge in his book *The Fifth Discipline: The Art & Practice of The Learning Organization*[33] says in his chapter on "The Principle of Leverage:"

> To me, the bottom line of systems thinking is leverage—seeing where actions and changes in structure can lead to significant, enduring improvements. Often, leverage follows the principle of economy of means: where the best results come not from large-scale efforts but small, well-focused actions. Our non-systemic ways of thinking are so damaging specifically because they consistently lead us to focus on low-leverage changes: we focus on symptoms where the stress is greatest. We repair or ameliorate the symptoms. But such efforts only make matters better in the short run, at best, and worse in the long run.

Senge goes on to say that the art of systems thinking lies in seeing patterns where others see only events and forces to react to—seeing the forest as well as the trees. Mikel recognized that applying the concept of leverage is the difference between continuous improvement and breakthrough improvement. The Breakthrough Strategy and the application of the concept of leverage will guide us to understanding and discovering that those factors having the most impact are going to distinguish extraordinary thinkers from ordinary thinkers and will lead us to breakthrough results.

Chapter 22
Measurement Brings About Knowledge

The importance of Measurement should be obvious. After all, it is one of the phases of the ICOV Model of RDMAICSI. In Six Sigma, our goals are broken down into projects and converted to measurements that are analyzed to create improvements.

Mention the word measurement to Mikel, and you were likely to get the following response:

> Lord Kelvin said, *"If we cannot express what we know in the form of measurements, then our knowledge is of a meager and unsatisfactory kind."*

Mikel would then likely follow up with what he called Harry's corollary to Lord Kelvin's quote on measurement:

We don't know what we don't know.

We won't know until we measure.

We don't measure what we don't value.

We don't value what we don't measure.

We don't measure what we don't question.

We don't know what we don't question.

We can't do what we don't know.

If you can't express what you know in the form of measurements, you don't really know much about it. And if you don't know much about it, you can't control it, and if you can't control it, you are at the mercy of chance. And if you are at the mercy of chance, why bother with it? You are sure not going to be able to improve it.

Why is it we don't know? Mikel would say, "Simply because we don't know. We don't know what we don't know. On the flip side of that: Do we really know what we know? Or do we just think we know?" Mikel's point is that without measurements, we can't know for sure, and if we think we know and don't have measurements, we really don't know what we think we do.

A core belief of Six Sigma is that we make decisions based upon facts that can be verified. And one of the best ways of verification is through measurement. The basis of science is the ability to replicate something. The extent of accuracy and precision to which we can replicate something is dependent upon measurement. Through measurement comes knowledge and validation, which empowers us to seek improvement.

Mikel developed what he called the "Success Triangle," consisting of Measurement, Knowledge, and Questions.

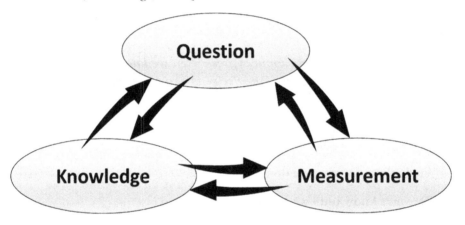

Figure 29 Success Triangle

Mikel said, "I always like the word question because of the word quest. Questioning is a quest for knowledge. And the quest for knowledge is enabled through measurement. Through questioning the measurements, we are forced to question our knowledge. By questioning our knowledge, we'll have breakthrough and be able to transition ourselves to an improved state."

Questioning is the basis of investigation, of interrogation. We gain a depth of understanding and scope of knowledge through measurements. When we gather measurements, our knowledge increases, which leads to more questions. The gained knowledge is what drives us to better decisions. In this sense, it's not what we know that gets us in trouble; it's what we don't know. So Six Sigma is the continual pursuit into what we don't know, that is knowable, acknowledging some things perhaps are not knowable.

It doesn't matter where we start in the Success Triangle. We can start with a question. That question, in turn, leads to measurement. That measurement, in turn, leads to knowledge which brings about more questions in a continuing cycle. If we start with measurements, taking measurements could cause us to formulate questions. As the questions are formulated, new measurements emerge. As those measurements emerge, knowledge is created. Likewise, knowledge could drive questions that are resolved by measurements, or knowledge could drive measurements that lead to more questions. Any path is possible. Knowledge, Measurement, Questions are interconnected. As Mikel would say, "It's a self-feeding bear."

For every action, we need to define our success criteria. Some may be as simple as "It is done." Most are likely to be more ambiguous. It is the ambiguous actions that need a measure of success defined in advance. The more objective the measurement the better. We need to manage by fact, not feelings. Feelings are not verifiable. Not that feelings should be discarded, but they should undoubtedly be tempered by facts that can be validated through measurement.

As noted previously, our values are what drive us, whether in a commercial or personal situation. As such, we question and desire to verify those things that carry value and conversely don't measure those things that don't have value. Six Sigma links measurements with values that drive an organization's actions, which in turn set improvement in motion. Measurement is at the very core of breakthrough improvement. Unfortunately, too often, decisions become an intuitive, experiential, Zen-like affair without an objective measure as a baseline. We can't improve what we don't measure. We can't track what we don't measure. And if we think we have improved, we have no way to validate the improvement without measurement.

Measurement and thus knowledge are repeatable. We can go out and collect more measurements a second time and see if the same knowledge results. As we take progressive measurements and the same knowledge occurs time and time again, then we can say that knowledge is verified. That is one reason that measurement is so important in the concept of Six Sigma.

It is important to recognize that the same question invariably produces the same result. If we expect to change the result, we must change the question. We need to pursue the question that's related to what we don't know. In the previous discussion, we noted that answers are a function of questions, and by applying the concept of determinism, we should focus on the questions, not on the answer. We should be asking questions about the causes attributing to our desired effect. We know—or at least think we know—the effect is not satisfactory, or else we would not be focusing on it. The question is what we do not know. What are the causes contributing to the effect? Once we have determined the vital few causes, we are able to baseline and set stretch goals for them, and through measurement, we will be guided to breakthrough improvement. We will not be successful if we focus on the symptom while asking the same questions over and over.

Therefore, the key to the driving need underlying Six Sigma is to measure. Lord Kelvin was absolutely right: "If we cannot express what we know in the form of measurements, then our knowledge is of a meager and unsatisfactory kind." And of course, Mikel's corollary to that is, "If you don't know much about it, you can't control it. If you can't control it, then you are at the mercy of chance. If you are at the mercy of chance, why bother?"

When we look into what we don't know, it generates some anxiety. Good leadership is to have people looking to what they don't know constantly. When we look at things we don't know, we tend to discover and find out more things that we do know. This is part of learning.

Chapter 23
Transformative Change

Mikel rarely discussed Transformation directly, even when introducing it as a Big Idea in the ICRAtic Value Creation Strategy. However, the word Transformation and the concept of Transformation are used throughout his writings.

Transformation means to make a marked or dramatic change. We find the idea of Transformation in Mikel's writing expressed in four forms:

- Data Transformation
- The function in the Deterministic Reasoning, $Y = f(X)$
- Transformation as a synonymous term with Breakthrough
- Transformation as a Big Idea

Before engaging with a potential Six Sigma client, Mikel always assessed their readiness to engage in the journey. The first question he always asked was, "Are you ready for an outright transformation?" Mikel did not want to get involved in organizations that were looking to tweak their business; he wanted to engage with organizations that were looking for a marked or dramatic change. He wanted to engage with organizations that desired to follow him along a pathway leading to Breakthrough (Transformation). When Mikel developed The Great Discovery, Transformation was again the objective of his thought process. Mikel said:

> The realization of your Catalyst will be transformative in nature. This means that once you achieve your Catalyst dream, your life, the lives of others, or the lives of your work team will shift to a higher state, to a higher quality of life. It is the power source that will give you the freedom of choice. The freedom to choose a way of living that is based on your innermost values.

When discussing breakthrough, Mikel linked the ideas of Determinism, Measurement, Leverage, and Transformation:

> Leverage, determinism, measurement, and transformation interact to create breakthrough.
>
> - Leverage in this context means that applying a small bit of force (Black Belts) focused on a fulcrum (Six Sigma) can move large organizations if the lever is long enough. We can leverage ideas from one unit to another. In other words, using what is learned from one project can make it faster and easier to replicate that project elsewhere.
>
> - Determinism says, you must accept that outputs, or effects, are determined by input, causes. This idea is represented as $Y = f(X) + e$ with the Outputs (Y) being the dependent variables, while the Inputs (X) are the independent variables (allowing error, e). Keeping the X's in control delivers the required result, Y.
>
> - Measurement means understanding the capability of your measuring device to pick up a real difference in what you are measuring. Six Sigma forces the management to properly measure the data.
>
> - We think in terms of Transformation, understanding the nature and impact of error, grasping the importance of probability, and increasing business power through dramatic change.
>
> Six Sigma is a deeply penetrating, broadly applied system for achieving quantum change, corporate transformation, and business breakthrough.

Mikel called his way of thinking The Breakthrough Strategy which we came to know as ICOV (RDMAICSI) and The Great Discovery. The objective of The Breakthrough Strategy models is Transformation based upon Values. The Breakthrough models themselves provide a pathway for all people in the organization To Learn to Think like a Leader, and the means to go from **Ordinary thinkers to extraordinary thinkers**.

We see Transformation in the ICRAtic Value Creation Strategy as the bridge between Configuration and Realization. It is Transformative Thinking that allows us to move beyond a conceptual idea to one that can be configured in such a way that it has scale, can be measured, and be realized in such a way that we know marked, dramatic breakthrough, and beneficial change has occurred.

As we move forward in our thinking we must focus on the Velocity of Value: delivering value in the shortest time possible.

Chapter 24
Power and Velocity

One of the definitions of Power is "possession of control, authority, or influence over others." Many think of Power, in the context of management or leadership, as being Power associated with rank or position, the ability to impose decisions authoritatively. I have two personal stories related to this concept from my early years as an executive:

> Soon after I was appointed Vice-President, I recognized that what would normally be casual comments to my managers were all of a sudden viewed not as suggestions but mandates. Nothing had changed but a title, but the impact of what I had to say all of a sudden was viewed differently. Many of my employees called me Mr. Alan. Alan would have been acceptable to me, but they wanted to show respect and had difficulty pronouncing my last name.

> While at a company picnic, a child of one of my employees asked, "What is your name?" I replied, "I'm Alan. What is your name?" His eyes got very large, and he said, "You're Mr. Alan?" I said, "Yes, but you can just call me Alan." He then said, "You are the person that signs my dad's paycheck." Signing checks was one of the trivial tasks that I had to do. In those days, our payroll checks were initiated remotely and printed on our local printer, so I had to literally sign those checks.

These two incidents happened in very close proximity and had a massive impact on my view of Power: "When you have power, you don't need to use it." Power attributable to authority or position has no place in Leadership.

$$\text{Power} = \frac{\text{Work}}{\text{Time}}$$

In physics, Power is the rate of doing work, Work over Time. It is in this sense that Power became a Big Idea both in the Ten Supreme Laws and in the ICRAtic Value Creation Strategy. Mikel said, "To make things happen, you need

Power, lots of it. To break down barriers along the way, you need Power. To have breakthrough, you need Power."

We can increase Power by either increasing the amount of work applied to an issue or by reducing the amount of time we take to resolve the issue.

Another equation for Power is

Power = Work x Velocity,

where Velocity is the speed of something in a given direction.

While Velocity only occurs as a Big Idea in the Ten Supreme Laws and not in ICRA, by its relationship to Power it is implied in ICRA. Mikel viewed Velocity as speed.

Mikel viewed Force as the depth of knowledge applied, i.e., Champions, Black Belts, Green Belts, Yellow Belts. He viewed Span as the breadth over which the knowledge was applied across the organization, i.e., how many people were provided knowledge through training. Mikel related Power to Force times Span over Time, which is discussed in more detail in the last section of the book.

When applying the Big Ideas of Power and Velocity, Mikel's philosophy was that you need to disperse knowledge as deeply as possible by training people at the appropriate level; dispersing knowledge as wide as possible by training as many people as possible; and by doing so as fast as possible. From a broader sense, the philosophy of Power and Velocity are an integral part of Leadership in that all issues should be dealt with as deeply and as widely as possible and at the fastest possible speed.

In Mikel's later years, Velocity began to rise to the top of his list of Big Ideas with his focus on Value. He coined the term Velocity of Value. He realized that when working toward improvement and value creation, value was gained by increasing the speed at which the issue was attacked. Mikel relayed this message in his discussion of The Ten Supreme Laws associated with The Great Discovery:

> At the root of power is some kind of change and that change occurs over time. Remember, we call that Velocity. If we multiply that by the force behind it, we've got Power. When Knowledge is spread across a lot of people in a short period of time, you have Knowledge Power. The mechanism for spreading your message across the world is your change agent. A strong message spread across the world in a short period of time is Communications Power. When you can apply a

problem-solving system over a short period of time, you have Resolution Power.

The Catalyst is the power you need to get you to your life dream. A Catalyst dream is like a power source that energizes the appliances in your kitchen, such as a toaster, blender, coffee maker, and so on. While these appliances serve a distinct purpose in your life, they need electricity to function.

When you achieve your Catalyst dream, it's like starting a generator. Once started, the generator creates the electricity you need to energize the appliances of your life, so to speak. In other words, when your Catalyst dream is achieved, you are free to activate any or all of the values that are connected to that power source.

If we don't know, we cannot act.

If we cannot act, the risk of loss is high.

If we do know and act, the risk can be managed.

If we do know and fail to act, we deserve the loss.

Chapter 25
Uncertainty and Risk

Fear of Uncertainty or Risk should never be an excuse for staying on the Calf-Path.

The Ten Supreme Laws include Uncertainty but not Risk, while the ICRAtic Value Creation Strategy includes Risk but not Uncertainty. In general language, uncertainty and risk tend to be used interchangeably, but there is a distinct difference. Reviewing Mikel's work on Uncertainty and Risk, he clearly did not use the words interchangeably; however, he sometimes blurs the line between the two and did not state explicitly why he used Uncertainty in the Ten Supreme Laws and Risk in the ICRAtic Value Creation Strategy.

To try to understand Mikel's selection of Uncertainty and Risk as a Big Idea, let's first look at the definition and roots of the two words:

> *Merriam-Webster* defines Uncertainty, a noun, as simply being uncertain. That doesn't help much, so we need to look at the word uncertain, which is an adjective. Uncertain describes something that is not known; beyond doubt; without certain knowledge; not clearly identified or defined; not constant; indefinite. An etymology search indicates that Uncertainty has its roots from the 1300's.
>
> Risk, when used as a noun, indicates the possibility of loss; someone or something that creates a hazard; the chance of loss or the perils to the subject matter; the degree of probability of such loss. Risk was first used in the mid-1600's, associated with danger. Risk became more prominent in the 1900's, associated with investment.

Frank H. Knight's *Risk, Uncertainty, and Profit* published in 1921[34] is an often-cited source in distinguishing the difference between Uncertainty and Risk in a modern economic context. However, in his book, Knight notes his work is built on previous work in the area of insurance, speculation, and entrepreneurship dating to as early as 1895. Many references to Knight's work include the diagram shown below.

Figure 30 Uncertainty and Risk

The diagram in Figure 30 is not part of Knight's original work and the source is unknown. However, it does a good job of simplifying Knight's very detailed writing which is beyond the scope of this book. Some observations about this diagram:

1) All risks are uncertain; however, not all uncertainties are risks.

2) Uncertainty is randomness with unknowable probabilities, while Risk is randomness with knowable probabilities.

3) Simply stated, uncertainty is that which is unknown about something and certainty is what we know about something. Uncertainty is a lack of complete certainty. The outcome of any event is entirely unknown, and it cannot be measured or guessed as there is no background information available.

4) We also know that Uncertainty plus Certainty equals 100%. This reflects all possible options for any given situation. We also know the Probability of Certainty and Risk combine to equal 100%.

I would suggest a modified diagram, as shown in Figure 31 below.

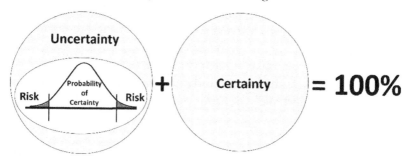

Figure 31 Uncertainty, Probability, Risk, Certainty

- The diagram is expanded to show that Uncertainty (what is not known) plus Certainty (what is known) is equal to 100%.

- The circle of Uncertainty represents what is not known.

- The probability distribution represents lack of complete certainty but there is enough information to measure, which allows us to predict certainty and the risk of not being certain.

Paraphrasing Knight, knowledge, in a sense, is variable in degree. The essence of the situation is action according to opinion, of greater or lesser foundation and value, neither entire ignorance nor complete and perfect information, but partial knowledge. This takes us back to the Success Triangle of Knowledge, Questions, and Measurement. Through questioning, we are often able to collect information that allows us to develop distributions that move us from Uncertainty to Risk. Once we measure, we can calculate the Risk and increase our Knowledge.

It is essential to note probability cannot be computed from a single unique instance. A single instance could simply be happenstance and allows no means to calculate error. As we make repeated measurements, we start to develop error. Error is the uncertainty that exists in those measurements. We can reduce the error in the risk calculation by increasing the number of samples.

Let's now look at what Mikel had to say about Uncertainty and Risk and how he blurred their use. We will look at both his statements and redevelop each statement using the distinction between Uncertainty and Risk.

- We noted that one of the three primary concepts of Six Sigma is Variation Reduction. Mikel stated, "Variation is the enemy. It constitutes uncertainty. And we want to remove uncertainty. We want to make our processes operate as certain as possible." Uncertainty is what we don't know, and we use the Success Triangle to discover and reduce it. Once we have discovered something, we can then measure and calculate Risk. Mikel's statement would be clearer when stated like this: **Variation is the enemy and correlates to the Risk. We want to reduce Risk and make our processes operate as certain as possible.**

- "If your risk is uncertain, then how in the world are you going to steer the ship called your business. So once again, we come to understand that measurement is everything to defining this relationship, which is what Six Sigma is all about." Risk is actually the likelihood of being Uncertain. In other words, Risk is a subset of Uncertainty and is the likelihood that our probability calculation is wrong. If we are wrong, we are uncertain. Let's restate this as follows: **If you are Uncertain or if you are unable to calculate the Risk of Uncertainty, then how in the world are you going to steer the ship called your business?**

- "The more we can use facts over intuition, the more we can integrate facts and intuition in a congruent way, the more certainty we will have. We will have less uncertainty and more confidence. What can be done to reduce uncertainty? Increase the quantity and quality of our knowledge, experience, data, information, feedback, coaching, and technology." Certainty is what we know to be true. This means: **We can also increase our Certainty using statistics to calculate the Probability of Certainty for our hypotheses.**

Six Sigma historically focused on the idea of defects. That's an *a posteriori*, after the fact, view of improvement, i.e., analysis of defects focuses on something that has already occurred. Instead, we want to take an a priori approach, proactive. Instead of focusing on defects, Generation III Six Sigma and The Great Discovery focus on value through the reduction of risk. We reduce Risk by increasing the quantity and quality of our knowledge, experience, data, information, feedback, coaching, technology, and analysis.

Uncertainty can induce fear, create conflict, and increase indecisiveness. Uncertainty often obscures breakthrough. For example, the main problem may be well known, but once we start pursuing the causes, branches of uncertainty often obscure a resolution. As leaders, we must ask the right questions, the questions that will encourage our team to pursue answers to the unknown causes by investigation through measurement, facts, and data. As Mikel would say, "We only get the facts if we've asked the right questions. As leaders, our role is to provide through questions 'the yellow brick road' that will lead us to breakthrough to increased value."

Remember that we don't know what we don't know. Good leadership always guides people into looking for what they don't know, encouraging them to discover new knowledge. Mikel often said, "When a leader is on target with their questions, anxiety will most often be present." A strong leadership principle is decreasing Uncertainty through the Success Triangle and further reducing Uncertainty through statistical analysis of Risk. By following this principle, the probability of success is greatly enhanced.

Chapter 26
Complexity: Nodes and Connections

Complexity has to do with the total number Critical to Quality Characteristics (CTQ) in a product or service. If the process capability is fixed and the number of CTQ's increases, we are going to see more defects. Let's look at flipping a coin. Assuming the coin is fair, there should be a 50% probability of flipping a head and a 50% probability of flipping a tail—half the time we will flip a head, and half the time we will flip a tail. If we were to flip a second coin, it too would have a 50/50 probability. But what about the probability of flipping two heads in a row? The probability of two heads in a row is the probability of flipping a head on the first attempt times the probability of flipping a head on the second attempt. In the case of a fair coin, this would be 50% times 50% or 0.5 x 0.5 = 0.25 (25%). The probability of flipping three heads in a row would be 0.5 x 0.5 x 0.5 = 0.125 (12.5%) and so forth for consecutive heads in a row. So, the more consecutive attempts, the lower the probability of success.

Instead of thinking about a coin, let's think about CTQ's. What if the probability of creating each "good" CTQ is 95%? This means if we have only one CTQ, the probability of having a good product is 95%. What if there are two CTQ's? The probability of a good product, where both CTQ's are good, is 0.95 x 0.95 = 0.9025 (90.25%). What about the probability of a good product if there are three CTQ's? The probability of all three CTQ's being good is 0.95 x 0.95 x 0.95 = 0.8573 (85.73%). The more CTQ's, the lower the probability of them all being jointly good. In other words, as the number of steps, or operations, or part counts, or anything in a system, increases in number, given a constant complexity, the aggregate joint likelihood of success goes down. In order to improve the likelihood of success, the capability must be increased and/or complexity must be reduced.

The table and chart below (Figure 32) show yields for 3, 4, 5, and 6 Sigma levels of performance for complexity levels of 1, 10, 100, 1,000, and 10,000 CTQ's. As complexity (the number of CTQ's) increases for any given level of capability, (Sigma Level of performance) yields drop. As capability decreases for any given level of complexity, yields fall. When process capability is low, the influence of complexity is quite high. For example, at Three Sigma, yield drops to near zero at only 100 CTQ's. However, as capability increases, we become more robust, more resilient to the influence of complexity. At Six Sigma, yield is 96.66% at 10,000 CTQ's. We can improve yields by either increasing capability (yield) or reducing complexity. We want to start at the design level by decreasing complexity.

			CTQ's				
Sigma Level	DPMO	Yield	1	10	100	1,000	10,000
3	66,807	93.3193%	93.319%	50.086%	0.099%	0.000%	0.000%
4	6,210	99.3790%	99.379%	93.961%	53.639%	0.197%	0.000%
5	233	99.9767%	99.977%	99.768%	97.700%	79.243%	9.763%
6	3	99.9997%	100.000%	99.997%	99.966%	99.661%	96.659%

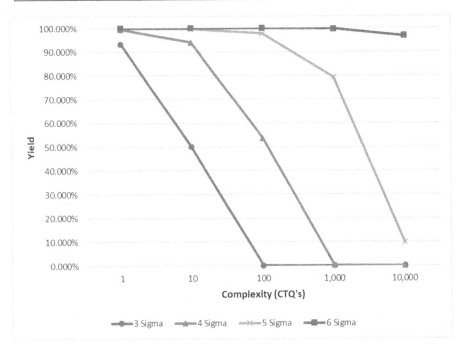

Figure 32 Capability and Complexity

From a leadership perspective, we want to reduce complexity by simplifying the design, designing in functionality, and designing out interdependency. Complexity is made up of nodes and connections, so we want to design in nodes that have a lot of function and design out nodes and connections wherever possible in order to simplify the design. If interconnections are equal to zero, we have a linear system of nodes where the nodes are just a simple part count. But when they're all interconnected and interrelated, like a network of things, then you have a complex system. Complexity is very difficult to manage, very difficult to monitor, very difficult to report on, and extremely difficult to improve.

When addressing any issue, we need to look at reducing complexity. This is not only from the perspective of the system itself but also in the thought process. In deterministic thinking, we look to define only the Vital Few X's and put aside the Trivial Many. We focus on the things that have the most impact. The reduction of complexity is also at the heart of root cause analysis. As Leaders, we must work our way through the web of complexity and put our efforts toward those things that matter.

Constancy is a never-ending passion to set unconstrained dreams and striving to achieve your breakthrough.

Chapter 27
Constancy of Purpose

The Big Idea of Constancy or Constancy of Purpose was the first of fourteen points[35] identified by W. Edwards Deming who is considered one of the great thought leaders of management. These fourteen points are often referred to as the Deming Model of Quality Management. Much has been written about Deming's fourteen points, so we will focus strictly on the first point "Create constancy of purpose for improving products and services."

In his book, *Out of Crisis,*[36] Deming noted: Constancy of Purpose means acceptance of obligations, such as the following:

- Innovate. Allocate resources for long-term planning.
- Put resources into Research and Education.
- Constantly improve the design of products and services.

Deming's Constancy of Purpose advocated considering the organization as a system and incorporation of long-term thinking. Mikel agreed with this perspective. However, Constancy as a Big Idea is to maintain an ever-lasting pressure toward the improvement of Values, as he explains in his presentation on the Ten Supreme Laws.

> Adherence, Dependability, Determination, Permanence, Perseverance, Regularity, Stability, Steadiness, Tenacity, Uniformity. Constancy is a never-ending commitment to setting your plan, goals, and dreams, and reaching out to achieve breakthrough—what you want. Constancy of purpose is everything. We are dedicated to the mission and are resolved that we will achieve breakthrough. We want to believe in our team and methodology. We want to have effort—a constant push day after day in a consistent, steady way.

It doesn't matter whether we are trying to change something in our personal life in order to improve our Values or whether we are trying to address existing

Value issues in an organization. Mikel's point was that we have to understand our Values, be able to determine and prioritize the gaps in our Values, and push forward aggressively with Constancy.

One of the things we often forget is that we are always supposed to approach thinking about Values without constraint. This means we are not to put any limitations on our thoughts. Thoughts without limitation lead to Innovation. In this way, Constancy is a vital element in the ICRAtic Value Creation Strategy as well as the Breakthrough Strategy. If we are going to Innovate new solutions, it takes Constancy, always thinking without constraints, and including Innovative thought in everything that we do.

ICRAtic Value Creation Strategy

and

Integration of Big Ideas

Knowledge involves belief, but not all belief is based on knowledge.

Chapter 28
Strategy – Innovation – Leadership

The first two sections of the book focused on improving Leadership skills as they relate to problem solving and thinking deeper with regard to known variables. This section focuses on Creation of Value through Innovation, Imagination, Vision. You pick your word; but Leaders must be able to think about what is not as well as what is. This section of the book will advance your Leadership Thinking to that advanced level.

Giant Steps in Management: Creating Innovations That Change the Way We Work,[37] is a book which was published in 2008 and identifies the 50 top management innovations in the last 150 years, one of which is Six Sigma.

The authors note:

> Today we typically make a clear distinction between *strategy,* which refers to the choices firms make about where and how they play in the marketplace, and *innovation,* which refers to the implementation of new products, services, businesses and working practices. But they are two tightly interlinked concepts because both are concerned with how the firm adapts to its changing business chapter.

The authors define Management Innovation as "A company's ability to affect fundamental changes in its own internal way of working." However, they decide to treat strategy and innovation as a singular concept:

> In this book, we have developed models that apply both to organizations of all types and our personal lives. So let's narrow the above definition even further: **Innovation is the ability to affect fundamental change in the way we work.**

While researching for this book, several words were filtered out as the real purpose behind Mikel's concepts of The Breakthrough Strategy, Big Ideas, and ICRA. These words are Vision, Imagination, Creativity, Innovation, Change,

Strategy, and Leadership. There may be other words we could add to the list, but let's focus on these. We will start by looking at the dictionary definitions.[13] Admittedly, I chose certain portions of the definitions to make a point:

- **Vision:** a thought, concept, or object formed by the imagination; a manifestation to the senses of something immaterial; the act or power of imagination; unusual discernment or foresight; mode of seeing or conceiving.

- **Imagination:** the act or power of forming a mental image of something not present to the senses or never before wholly perceived in reality; creative ability; the ability to confront and deal with a problem; the thinking or active mind.

- **Creativity:** to bring into existence; to produce or bring about by a course of action or behavior; to produce through imaginative skill.

- **Innovation:** the introduction of something new; to introduce as, or as if new; to do something in a new way; to effect a change in; to make changes.

- **Change:** to make different; to give a different position, course, or direction; to replace; to undergo a modification.

- **Strategy:** the science and art of employing forces… to afford the maximum support of adopted policies; a careful plan or method.

- **Leadership:** to direct on a course or in a direction; to serve as a channel for; to direct the operations, activity, or performance of; to bring to some conclusion or condition; to guide someone or something along a way.

There is no doubt we could go through and pick the definitions of these words apart in order to support an argument that each word is distinct and different. In research for this book I have had many conversations and communications with peers who are experts in Leadership. It seems that while we agree on many topics, each of us has certain "key words" that we wish the other used or certain "concepts" that don't align completely. I have come to realize that we tend to focus on our differences, which keeps us from joining together to form a singular philosophy as opposed to working together to formulate, as the Pareto Principle would state, the 80% in which we are in agreement.

I am turned off by the title *Giant Steps in Management: Creating Innovations That Change the Way We Work* because I don't personally believe Managerial Skills and Leadership Skills are synonymous. However, it is silly to set aside the points made by the authors on Innovation just because I don't like the inclusion of "Management" in the title.

I'm not going to argue that each of these words are synonyms although the dictionary lists some as being so. I'm just arguing that in the context of this book and many other books using these words in their titles, chapters, or concepts, the words are similar enough that we should quit squabbling about the trivial many and focus on the vital few.

Benchmarking is a competitive tool used to uncover what we do well and not so good.

Chapter 29
ICRA Introduction

Research in Mikel's computer archive indicates that Mikel started working on the ICRAtic Value Creation Strategy in 2002. This is consistent with the inclusion of ICRA in Mikel's MindPro Lean Six Sigma training released in 2003, and the publication of the ICRAtic Value Creation Strategy in Chapter 7 (The Science of Value Creation) in *The Six Sigma Fieldbook*,[4] which was authored by Mikel Harry and DuPont's Six Sigma Champion Don R. Linsenmann. While the *Fieldbook* carries a 2006 copyright, the DuPont implementation began in 1998.

As we have discussed previously, Six Sigma started with a focus on quality in the 1980s at Motorola and evolved to a focus on cost reduction in the 1990s at General Electric. For DuPont's implementation in the 2000s, DuPont's champions pioneered a new focus for Six Sigma aimed at stimulating top-line-growth, while maintaining a strong focus on quality and cost reduction. They wanted to retain what was learned at Motorola and General Electric but expand the envelope by also targeting growth in revenue and market share simultaneously. DuPont's implementation strategy was labeled by Mikel as Generation III Six Sigma.

Mikel identified the focus of quality at Motorola as being a focus on the customer. Motorola was losing customers to Japanese competition because of quality issues. The implementation at General Electric retained a focus on quality levels but established the main focus on improving the bottom line. Quality standards had started to become an essential requirement for doing business, and General Electric wanted to direct their Six Sigma implementation on the bottom line. Mikel described Generation II Six Sigma at General Electric as being focused on the provider. DuPont wanted more! DuPont wanted to retain quality levels (which had become a requirement just to be in business) and to retain a focus on cost reduction aimed at the bottom line, while simultaneously focusing on the top-line growth. Mikel described Generation III Six Sigma as being a focus on both the customer and the provider.

The new paradigm for Generation III Six Sigma was business breakthrough which Mikel described as a focus on Value where both the customer and the provider realize value in every critical aspect of the business relationship.

Value is the equivalency of exchange in the Need-Do interaction between a customer and a provider. As Mikel said, "In other words, Six Sigma can not only drive a persuasive and dramatic reduction in defects, reduce costs, and enhance revenue, but can also create value on a broad and deep scale."

Many myths about Six Sigma had developed over the years and many are still prevalent:

- Six Sigma is good at driving quantum change in the mechanical aspects of business operations but not as effective in driving the creative aspects of business innovation.

- Six Sigma works better in manufacturing divisions than it does in R&D, procurement, sales, legal, marketing, and other functional areas.

- Six Sigma is a powerful tool for breakthrough in data-rich environments but not as powerful in the more ethereal, idea-driven realms of business.

- Six Sigma is an elitist strategy, available to only large corporations and not very usable by medium and small companies, or by the majority of non-management employees of large corporations.

- It takes more time to embed Six Sigma in non-manufacturing arenas, where processes are more fluid, organic, and non-repeatable.

DuPont's champions were aware of these myths and challenged Mikel as he led the implementation with Linsenmann. Mikel knew that in order to meet the challenge he needed to develop a new model which was first published in the *Fieldbook*, labeled the ICRAtic Value Creation Strategy as shown in Figure 8 and duplicated here for convenience. The model was based upon the four stages of Innovation, Configuration, Realization, and Attenuation and a set of twelve (12) Big Ideas or principles: Need, Idea, Measurement, Uncertainty, Value, Opportunity, Determinism, Leverage, Power, Transformation, Complexity, and Risk. The Big Ideas are internal to and surround the ICRA concept of business improvement.

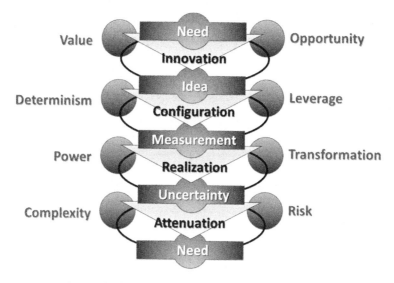

Figure 8 The ICRAtic Value Creation Strategy

Notice that the ICRAtic Value Creation Strategy starts and ends with the Big Idea of Need. The *Fieldbook* notes:

When business innovates, it begins by attempting to address a need or a negative gap between what is customers experience and what they expect. The business then turns to Big Ideas of value and opportunity to generate ideas to meet that need. These ideas are then leveraged and measured as they are tested in an ideal model of value creation.

After a business creates and realizes value (to a greater or lesser extent), it improves its processes by reducing its uncertainty, complexity, and risk.

Basically, a business innovates through the science of thinking, configures itself through the science of planning, realizes its potential through the science of doing, and attenuates itself through the science of improvement.

> *Data is not information until it is interrogated.*

Chapter 30
ICRA and The Big Ideas

The Six Sigma Fieldbook explains the ICRAtic Value Creation Strategy in great detail. I obtained permission to present those details in this chapter verbatim as they were presented in the *Fieldbook*:

> Each Big Idea breaks into a set of two phrases, one high-level elaboration and the other a more descriptive but still general statement of the action. Only by stringing the Big Ideas together does a leader begin to understand the underlying code of business success. While there is scientific progress of thought moving through the major phases of the Value Creation Strategy, there is also a progression of thought within each phase as the Big Ideas come into play.

This concept is portrayed in the following table, which is presented in the *Fieldbook*:

STRATEGY FOR VALUE CREATION				
Phase	**Big Ideas**			
Innovation	Proclaim	To declare	Need	Deprived state
	Prospect	To explore	Value	Equivalent exchange
	Pursue	To search	Opportunity	Favorable conditions
Configuration	Purity	To refine	Idea	Conceptual model
	Pattern	To design	Determinism	Effectual cause
	Parlay	To exploit	Leverage	Mechanistic advantage
Realization	Prescribe	To establish	Measurement	Scaled quantity
	Provide	To supply	Power	Change capability
	Perfect	To improve	Transformation	Change process
Attenuation	Prohibit	To prevent	Uncertainty	Unknown state
	Paralyze	To disable	Complexity	Confounded connections
	Prune	To abate	Risk	Loss exposure

Figure 33 Big Ideas Integrated into ICRA

The following table will help to understand the explanation of how the Big
Ideas integrate into the ICRAtic Value Creation Strategy:

STRATEGY FOR VALUE CREATION				
Phase	**Big Ideas**			
	Proclaim	To declare	Need	Deprived state
Innovation	Prospect	To explore	Value	Equivalent exchange
	Pursue	To search	Opportunity	Favorable conditions

In all business, we engage in innovation by identifying a need to be
addressed or a deprived state. Recognizing that business is a "need-do"
interaction between the customer and the provider, we then explore the
equivalency of value exchange in that interaction.

Next, a business must search for conditions that are favorable to
configuring and realizing the envisioned value proposition. When
conditions are properly identified and aligned, we create the
opportunity to realize the mutual exchange of value, which in turn
satisfies the need and relieves the deprived state. In theory, this
exchange fulfills the customer's need while generating profit for the
provider.

The exchange in value between the customer and the provider does not happen
in reality until the remaining phases are fulfilled.

STRATEGY FOR VALUE CREATION				
Phase	**Big Ideas**			
	Purity	To refine	Idea	Conceptual model
Configuration	Pattern	To design	Determinism	Effectual cause
	Parlay	To exploit	Leverage	Mechanistic advantage

When we engage in configuration, we refine a conceptual model of
how we intend to create and exchange value: We refine our idea, or
ideal, for meeting a need in a profitable way. We then design a system
of effectual causation (Y-X chain) for bringing our idea into the real
world. Configuration should take the fuzziness of an idea and
document it in the form of a tangible design that can be seen,
discussed, and modified by others.

The configuration should exploit the vital few factors that provide the most
leverage.

Finally, it should align the factors that will help in closing the
satisfaction gap—bringing about a deliverable that will satisfy the needs
and expectations of the customer while satisfying the goals of the
provider.

STRATEGY FOR VALUE CREATION				
Phase	**Big Ideas**			
Realization	Prescribe	To establish	Measurement	Scaled quantity
	Provide	To supply	Power	Change capability
	Perfect	To improve	Transformation	Change process

In the realization phase, we bring our plan into real-time. A measurement must
be established by which to gauge progress as we bring our grand plan to its
potential to its reality:

> As we put our plan into operation, we invariably discover that certain
> conditions are not being optimized. Certain deliverables fall short of
> their expectations.

So we look for ways to grow productivity by closing any gaps that remain:

> In other words, we toggle back and forth between configuration and
> realization until the bugs have been worked out of the system.

Toggling between configuration and realization increases our power for closing
the gaps and improve our change capability, which allows us to perfect our
transformation of the process.

STRATEGY FOR VALUE CREATION				
Phase	**Big Ideas**			
Attenuation	Prohibit	To prevent	Uncertainty	Unknown state
	Paralyze	To disable	Complexity	Confounded connections
	Prune	To abate	Risk	Loss exposure

In the attenuation phase:

> We attenuate or lessen the uncertainty, complexity, and risk around the
> 'knobs' (X's) that control the most variables in a given value chain. We
> reduce our distance between entitlement and a given need.

In fact, we reduce uncertainty, complexity, and risk all the way up and down the
chain. In doing so, corporations can sustain short-term and long-term
capability:

In other words, it gives corporations the ability to produce a high-quality product or service—a deliverable—consistently over time.

In summary, the value creation cycle begins with the innovation of an idea for meeting a need. We then move on to the configuration of an actual design for doing so. After this, we rely on the process of realization to create value. Finally, we lessen complexity, uncertainty, and risk in order to continue the gains we have made. This is the cycle of value creation.

The value creation is continuously repeated to address prioritized needs.

The table of Big Ideas Integrated into ICRA is concise, and the discussion in the *Fieldbook* is complete. However, I found it difficult to follow and have broken the table and discussion into sections so that text can be more easily connected with the contents of the table.

When the table is combined with the figure representing the ICRAtic Value Creation Strategy (Figure 8) repeated here once again for convenience, the relationship between the Big Ideas and the ICRA phases should be clear:

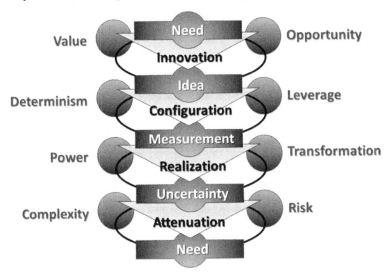

Figure 8 The ICRAtic Value Creation Strategy

- The Big Ideas of Need, Value, and Opportunity are associated with the Innovation Phase.

- The Big Ideas of Idea, Determinism, and Leverage are associated with the Configuration Phase.

- The Big Ideas of Measurement, Power, and Transformation are associated with the Realization Phase.

- The Big Ideas of Uncertainty, Complexity, and Risk are associated with the Attenuation Phase.

Management is the judicious use of control toward the attainment of an end.

Chapter 31
The Relationship Between ICRA and ICOV

The Six Sigma Fieldbook presents the relationship between ICRAtic Value Creation Strategy and ICOV: The Breakthrough Strategy, by adding the Breakthrough Strategy to Figure 33. The expanded table is shown below with the Big Idea elaborations omitted.

		STRATEGY FOR BREAKTHROUGH PERFORMANCE			
		Identification	Characterization	Optimization	Validation
STRATEGY FOR VALUE CREATION	Innovation	Need	Value	Opportunity	Innovation
	Configuration	Idea	Determinism	Leverage	Configuration
	Realization	Measurement	Power	Transformation	Realization
	Attenuation	Uncertainty	Complexity	Risk	Attenuation

The Twelve Big Ideas from ICRA are shaded.

Figure 34 Relationship Between ICRA and ICOV

While the combined chart was succinct, the relationship between ICRA and ICOV was likely not obvious to most readers of the *Fieldbook* since the *Fieldbook* does not identify ICOV as being the Breakthrough Strategy, except in the table. Plus ICOV is not specifically mentioned in the *Fieldbook*, but rather is mentioned only in word form in the chart as the Strategy for Breakthrough Performance: Identification, Characterization, Optimization, and Validation. As noted previously, very few Six Sigma practitioners have heard of either the ICRA or ICOV models. While ICRA and ICOV are both presented in Mikel's MindPro Lean Six Sigma Training developed in 2003, the *Fieldbook* is the only known publication of ICRA and there are no known publications of ICOV.

In the many years that I worked with Mikel, I only remember talking to Mikel about ICRA and ICOV in separate discussions. Although I have read the *Fieldbook* and have been through the MindPro training many times, it was not until I was researching for this book that I realized the true connection, one I likely missed due to the page layout in the *Fieldbook*. While reading the *Fieldbook* this particular paragraph caused me to pause:

> As Six Sigma shifts from Generation II to Generation III, it becomes less focused on defect reduction and more focused on value creation. In the process, the Breakthrough Strategy is integrated into a larger strategy for creating value called ICRA.

Associated with the table in the *Fieldbook* showing the Relationship Between Value Creation and Breakthrough was a section titled "Value Creation and Breakthrough," which I have repeated verbatim below. Refer to Figure 8 (The ICRAtic Value Creation Strategy), Figure 33 (Big Ideas Integrated into ICRA) and Figure 35 (ICRA, Big Ideas, and Breakthrough) as you read the following excerpt.

VALUE CREATION AND BREAKTHROUGH

It is interesting to chart the Value Creation Strategy and the Big Ideas against the Breakthrough Strategy. When we do this, we can visualize in more detail how the Big Ideas connect the classic mind-set of the Breakthrough Strategy with the more progressive mind-set of the Value Creation Strategy.

During the value creation phase of innovation, for example, we identify a need by declaring a deprived state. We characterize value by exploring the equivalency of exchange, and we optimize by searching for favorable conditions. Finally, we validate or affirm that we have achieved the full intent of innovation. Only when this has been accomplished can we say that we have successfully completed a cycle of innovation, relative to a specific need, in a Six Sigma way.

As a value creation project leader moves from innovation to configuration, the task becomes one of identifying the ideas or refining the conceptual model to the point at which it becomes possible to design effectual causation. In turn, when we design effectual causation, we are characterizing the determinism that will bring about the desired change. We are designing, or configuring, a system of effectual causation relative to our value creation objective. During configuration, we are optimizing and leveraging our design by doing what we can to exploit the mechanistic advantage. Next, a project leader validates that the resulting design or plan has been configured in accordance with the Breakthrough Strategy and the intent of applicable Big Ideas.

We could continue this train of thought by outlining how the realization and attenuation phases of the Value Creation Strategy interface with the Breakthrough Strategy, but this should be evident from studying the Relationship Between Value Creation and the Breakthrough table. Moreover, there is more to be gained by looking deeply into the Big Ideas themselves—into the underlying concepts that make them operable. By doing so we can understand what each is made of and how they interact to create the *tsunami of reasoning* in the interest of achieving business breakthrough.

There it was, hidden in plain sight, but camouflaged even further with the last paragraph of the section, which deflects thought from the relationship of ICRA and ICOV to the importance of Big Ideas.

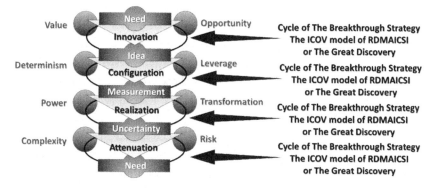

Figure 35 ICRA, Big Ideas, and Breakthrough

The key to understanding the relationship between ICRA and ICOV was pulling out the word **"Integrated"** in that paragraph: **"As Six Sigma shifts from Generation II to Generation III, it becomes less focused on defect reduction and more focused on value creation. In the process, the Breakthrough Strategy is integrated into a larger strategy for creating value called ICRA."** ICOV is literally integrated into the ICRA – The Breakthrough Strategy is repeated at each phase of ICRA, as shown in Figure 35.

It is important to distinguish the role of ICRA versus the role of ICOV. As noted in Chapter 6 of this book:

When compared to the original Logic Filter model which filters the total universe of all variables, ICRA looks at the universe of unknown variables to determine opportunities to innovate—invent or create something new—which will bring higher levels of satisfaction. We can think of ICRA as a model for creating Breakthrough of what might be and DMAIC as a model for creating Breakthrough in what is.

ICRA is a model for Value Creation – Innovation, whereas the Breakthrough Strategies of ICOV and The Great Discovery are models for creating Breakthrough via a prescribed recipe of problem solving. The Big Ideas, while shown explicitly in the ICRA model, are also important while engaging in the Breakthrough Strategy.

The organization of this book is consistent with Figure 35 and develops a full understanding of Mikel's way of thinking:

- Understand the Breakthrough Strategy presented both in the technical form of the ICOV model of RDMAICSI and the personal model of The Great Discovery. This is how leaders go about solving problems efficiently and effectively.

- Expand leadership thinking by incorporating the Big Ideas from the Ten Supreme Laws and ICRA. This allows you to investigate problems more profoundly and guides you in developing improvements.

- Go beyond addressing existing variables (What is) and start investigating new variables (What might be). Engage in Innovation, not the improvement of existing values but exploration and creation of new values.

Replication of observation leads to validity of experience.

Chapter 32
ICRA Update – An Unpublished Model

Recently an unpublished ICRA model was discovered in a slide deck, dated 2006. While *The Six Sigma Fieldbook* has a copyright of 2006 as well, the *Fieldbook* would have been written before the slide deck. The unpublished model is shown below.

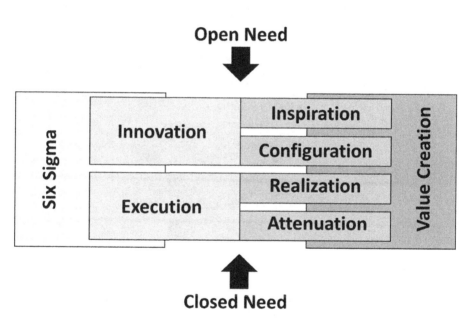

Figure 36 Unpublished ICRA Model

There are some differences that are important to note. This model uses Mikel's classic 2-4 categorization method, where there are two stages: Innovation, which breaks down into Inspiration and Configuration and Execution which breaks down into Realization and Attenuation. Further, it is important to note in the unpublished model: ICRA is *Inspiration,* Configuration, Realization, Attention; whereas, in the model published in the *Fieldbook*, ICRA is *Innovation,* Configuration, Realization, Attenuation.

The unpublished model indicates that ICRA is the means to move from Six Sigma which was focused on quality and cost reduction at the time to an expanded role of Value Creation. As Mikel often said, **Six Sigma evolved from a quality improvement program to a cost reduction program to a business breakthrough program.**

The unpublished model is consistent with the *Fieldbook's* ICRAtic Value Creation Strategy in that ICRA is bounded by the Big Idea of Need. We begin with Open Need and work to close that Need. The objective is to close the gap between the current state of the Need and the entitlement state of the Need.

If we add the two stages of Innovation and Execution and change Innovation to Inspiration as is indicated in the unpublished model, we would have a modified model, as shown in the figure below:

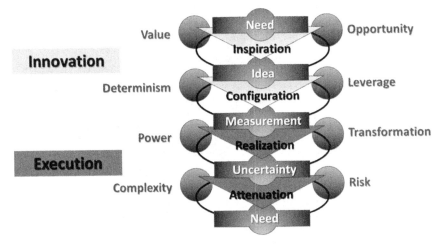

Figure 37 Modified ICRAtic Value Creation Strategy

Let's first discuss Mikel's substitution of Inspiration for Innovation. Mikel had moved on from ICRA and had started to work on The Great Discovery about this time period from which this unpublished slide deck was created. As we have discussed, Mikel worked very hard to use words in The Great Discovery that would be more familiar and more comfortable for lay people. It makes sense that he would substitute Inspiration for Innovation.

One might argue that while Inspiration is a better choice of words for a personal model, ICRA is a commercial model and thus, Innovation is a more appropriate word. I would ask, "Why does ICRA have to be just a commercial model?" As noted in Figure 35, either the commercial Breakthrough Strategy of

ICOV or the personal Breakthrough Strategy of The Great Discovery are compatible with ICRA. So, ICRA is a framework for Value Creation whether in the commercial or the personal application.

In the slide deck model shown in Figure 36, Mikel added the two root categories of Innovation and Execution. This is consistent with Mikel's The Great Discovery development, as noted in Figure 14, and repeated here for convenience:

Figure 14 The Great Discovery Expanded Model

While the ICRA steps of Innovation (Inspiration) and Configuration could be considered coming from the root of Innovation and Realization, and Attenuation could be considered to come from the root of Execution, I would like to propose a different model which more clearly defines the roles of ICRAtic Value Creation Strategy versus The Breakthrough Strategies of the ICOV model of RDMAICSI and The Great Discovery.

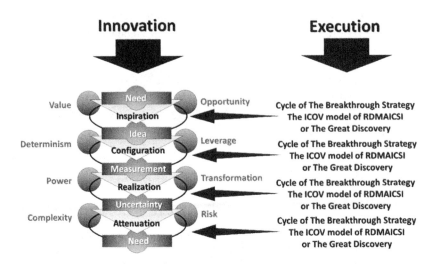

Figure 38 Dr. Mikel J. Harry Thought Process

The ICRAtic Value Creation Strategy is an Innovation Model, and the Breakthrough Strategy Models of ICOV (RDMAICSI) and The Great Discovery are Execution models. Viewed in this light, it makes more sense to change ICRA from Innovation – Configuration – Realization – Attenuation to *Inspiration* – **Configuration** – **Realization** – **Attenuation** as shown in Figure 38.

We described in Chapter 10 how the root categorizations of Innovation and Execution shown explicitly in The Great Discovery were also implicit in the ICOV Model of RDMAICSI. Figure 16 has been duplicated here for convenience:

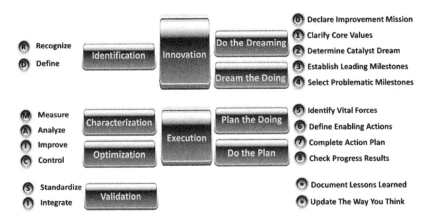

Figure 16 Comparing ICOV and The Great Discovery

Understanding how Innovation and Execution relate to each model can be confusing.

- Figure 38 shows that ICRA is an Innovation strategy and that The Breakthrough Strategies of ICOV (RDMAICSI) and The Great Discovery are Execution models that are applied at each phase of ICRA and, as such, we are executing each phase of the ICRAtic Value Creation Strategy.

- Figure 16 shows the Breakthrough Strategies of ICOV (RDMAICSI) and The Great Discovery which are Execution Strategies. However, within those Execution Strategies are Innovation and Execution phases.

So, whether the strategy is at its root an Innovation like ICRA or an Execution Strategy like ICOV or The Great Discovery, all require both Innovation and Execution level thinking.

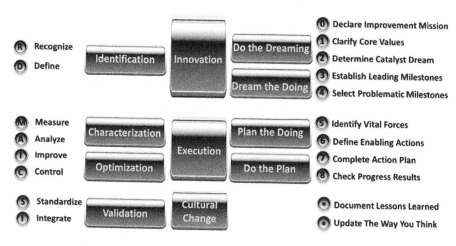

Figure 39 Cultural Change in the Breakthrough Strategies

If we take another step beyond Innovation and Execution, we also want to embed what we have learned into our culture or The Way You Think as shown in Figure 39 (Cultural Change in the Breakthrough Strategies) and Figure 40 (Cultural Change in the Innovation Strategy). Each of Mikel's Thought Models require Innovation Thinking, Execution Thinking, and an updating of the culture or The Way You Think based upon lessons learned. Understanding how these three levels of thinking are integrated is the key to the full understanding of Mikel's thought systems.

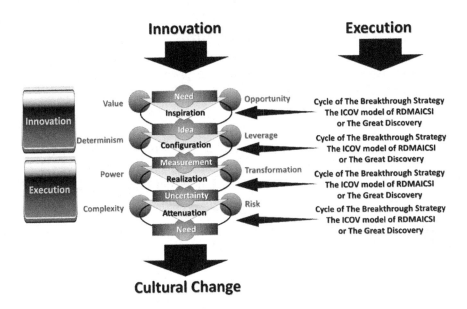

Figure 40 Cultural Change in the Innovation Strategy

Validation in the ICOV model includes Standardize and Integrate. As described in Chapter 7 and Figure 10 (which is duplicated below for convenience) Standardize and Integrate provide a means of taking lessons learned and integrating them into the culture in a way that the culture is dynamically updated. The Great Discovery Model does the same thing with the asterisk steps of Document Lessons Learned and Update The Way You Think.

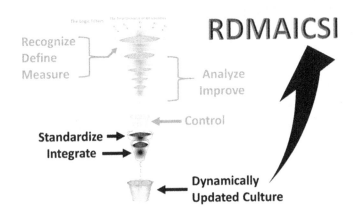

Figure 10 Standardize and Integrate Dynamically Updated Culture

For ICRA, Innovation includes Inspiration and Configuration phases. These two phases involve the creation of new values and then innovating how those new values will be integrated or configured. Integration or Configuration of new values is done by generating ideas that will decrease the need gap. ICRA then proceeds to the Realization and Attenuation phases, where a scale of success is determined through measurement, and uncertainty is removed by considering complexity and risk. The entire ICRAtic Value Creation Strategy serves to provide not only a cultural change but a cultural revolution.

Leaders recognize that each step of the thought process implements a model that requires both Innovation and Execution and has the final objective of Cultural Change by creating value, either through improvement of existing variables or creation of new ones.

Chapter 33
The Four Gospels of Value Creation: 4-G's

The Four Gospels of Value Creation are Growth, Goals, Gains, and Gaps. We set goals that will allow us to grow. As we strive to accomplish those goals, we make gains which close the gaps between our current state and our entitlement state. Mikel linked the 4 G's to the ICRAtic Value Creation Strategy as noted in the table below:

ICRA	Four Gospels
Innovate (Inspire)	Growth
Configure	Goals
Realize	Gains
Attenuate	Gaps

Figure 41 Relationship Between ICRA and the 4-G's

In Chapter 17 we noted that Mikel described Value as Utility, Availability (Access), and Worth. We noted that Mikel believed that Utility and Availability (Access) had to occur concurrently and we formed the definition: **Value is something of importance, measured along intellectual, emotional, and economic scales of Worth.**

It is important to keep in mind that ICRA is at the Innovation level. With ICRA we are not trying to accomplish Execution but simply trying to develop a framework, a plan, a strategic statement that sets the mission for Execution. Our focus in ICRA is on the macro level or what needs to be done rather than on the details required to execute or get it done.

Phase one of ICRA is Innovation (Inspiration). When integrated with the 4-G's we want to Innovate Growth. We innovate or inspire growth by recognizing our value needs. In Mikel's view, these needs would derive from Utility (form, fit, function) or Availability / Access (volume, location, timing). From our definition of Value, the needs would simply be **"something of importance"** to us. We search for change opportunities in those things of importance that will provide positive Breakthrough Change, which in turn will increase our Value.

In the Configuration Phase of ICRA, we Configure Goals, and we design and plan our goals in relation to the growth change opportunities that we identified for innovation. This includes understanding the current baseline, establishing an entitlement state, and then determining a target objective if it is not the entitlement state.

In phase 3 of ICRA, we develop a plan to Realize Gains. From a deterministic point of view, we know that $Y = f(X)$, Gains = f (Vital Few X's). In this phase, we identify at a macro level where we can leverage the change opportunities.

In the last phase of ICRA, we develop a strategy for Attenuating Gaps. Who are the key players, key departments, key business units that should be involved in reducing the gaps that will increase our value?

As shown in Figure 40, while ICRA is done at a macro level, we still engage the Execution thinking of ICOV (RDMAICSI) at every level.

Successful Innovation = f (Successful Execution); therefore, it is important that as Leaders, we employ Execution thinking even when we are focusing on Innovation.

ICRA is about the ability to innovate growth, configure the goals related to that growth, realize the gains associated with those goals, and attenuate the gaps and restraints that keep us from meeting and achieving those gains.

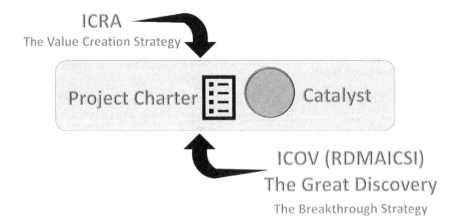

Figure 42 The Intersection Between Value Creation and Breakthrough

I like to view the Project Charter as the intersection of ICRAtic Value Creation Strategy and ICOV (RDMAICSI)—The Breakthrough Strategy, as shown in Figure 42. Similarly, when The Great Discovery is used as The Breakthrough Strategy instead of ICOV, the intersection is the Catalyst. The Project Charter or the Catalyst is where Innovation moves from just an Idea to an Execution state. The Project Charter or development of the Catalyst is where Innovation meets Execution. This is where compromises and negotiation of scope occur between the macro-side of Innovation and the micro-side of Execution. It is where successful Execution is planned so that successful Innovation can be realized.

Chapter 34
Core Competencies of Value Creation

Mikel developed sixteen core competencies that linked ICRA and the 4-G's to classical elements of an organization. By allowing executives to focus on these classical elements of an organization, they were able to grow their thinking using ICRA and the 4-G's instead of jumping in and focusing on Innovation abstractly.

ICRA	4-G's	Classical Focus			
		Market	Business	Product	Process
Innovate	Growth	Position	Strategy	Concepts	Methods
Configure	Goals	Channels	Operations	Features	Steps
Realize	Gains	Sales	Returns	Yield	Cycles
Attenuate	Gaps	Recoil	Cost	Defects	Variation

Figure 43 Sixteen Core Competencies

We can read the above table as follows:

- We Innovate Growth by focusing on:
  - Market Position
  - Business Strategy
  - Product Concepts
  - Process Methods
- We Configure Goals by focusing on:
  - Market Channels
  - Business Operations
  - Product Features
  - Process Steps
- We Realize Gains by focusing on:
  - Market Sales
  - Business Returns
  - Product Yield
  - Process Cycles

- We Attenuate Gaps by focusing on:
  o   Market Recoil
  o   Business Cost
  o   Product Defects
  o   Process Variation

It is not apparent from Mikel's table that all four phases of ICRA are used for each cell. ICRA and the 4-G's are shown in this table not as Thought Models but as a means of dissecting an organization using the terms from the ICRA and 4-G's models: Innovate Growth, Configure Goals, Realize Gains, and Attenuate Gaps.

For example, while Market Position is listed with respect to Innovate Growth, if we were to decide to focus on that single competency, we would use all four phases of the ICRA and 4-G's Thought Models—Innovate Growth, Configure Goals, Realize Gains, and Attenuate Gaps—with respect to how to improve Market Position.

Similarly, we could focus on a single column with respect to the Core Competencies. We could focus, for example, on all four levels with respect to Market: Position, Channels, Sales, and Recoil. Or we could focus across a single row by looking at strictly Innovation at the Market, Business, Product, and Process levels.

Again, it is important to separate ICRA and the 4G's, as presented in this chart, to help executives and champions dissect their organization versus ICRA and the 4-G's as Thought Models.

Mikel added to the table in Figure 44 to show the evolution of Six Sigma through the three generations.

ICRA	4-G's	Classical Focus				
		Market	Business	Product	Process	
Innovate	Growth	Position	Strategy	Concepts	Methods	Gen III
Configure	Goals	Channels	Operations	Features	Steps	Gen II
Realize	Gains	Sales	Returns	Yield	Cycles	Gen I
Attenuate	Gaps	Recoil	Cost	Defects	Variation	

Figure 44 Core Competencies and Generations of Six Sigma

The evolution of Six Sigma is seen more dramatically in the following table, which clearly shows the path of Quality program to a Cost Reduction program to a full Strategic Business program focused on both the Innovation and Execution of Business:

	Value Creation Competencies	Gen 0	Gen I	Gen II	Gen III
1	Innovating Growth Market Position				✓
2	Configuring Goals Market Channels				✓
3	Realizing Gains Market Sales				✓
4	Attenuating Gaps Market Recoil				✓
5	Innovating Growth Business Strategy				✓
6	Configuring Goals Business Operations			✓	✓
7	Realizing Gains Business Returns			✓	✓
8	Attenuating Gaps Business Cost			✓	✓
9	Innovating Growth Product Concepts				✓
10	Configuring Goals Product Features			✓	✓
11	Realizing Gains Product Yield		✓	✓	✓
12	Attenuating Gaps Product Defects	✓	✓	✓	✓
13	Innovating Growth Process Methods				✓
14	Configuring Goals Process Steps			✓	✓
15	Realizing Gains Process Cycles		✓	✓	✓
16	Attenuating Gaps Process Variation		✓	✓	✓

Figure 45 Evolution of Six Sigma

Mikel only developed the core competencies as they related to World Class Organizations, where the values with respect to Market, Business, Product, and Process are the primary divisors. However, core competencies could be developed for any topic using the ICRA and 4-G's models to dissect the topics. For example, The Great Discovery Model, while it can be used in the organizational structure for less technical people, is designed to engage at a personal level. It is beyond the scope of this book, but couldn't we develop an area of focus of the Values most important to us as chosen to replace Market, Business, Product, and Process and we develop core competencies for those values at the Innovate, Configure, Realize, and Attenuate levels? Could we not do the same thing if our overall topic was Team Building, Non-Profits, Religion, or any other topic? We could innovate an approach provided by the Value Creation Strategy of ICRA to develop those specialized core competencies for our topic of interest.

A fact is a form of information, but not all information is factual.

Chapter 35
The Phases of ICRA

As noted, The Breakthrough Strategies of the ICOV model of RDMAICSI and The Great Discovery are Execution strategies. The Breakthrough Strategies are the thought process that Leaders use to get things done. ICRA on the other hand is an Innovation strategy; the thought process of Leaders synonymous with: Vision, Imagination, Creativity, Innovation, Change, Strategy, and Leadership.

The Big Ideas from both ICRA and the Ten Supreme Laws are critical elements in a thought system. As Mikel said, "The Big Ideas help execute the work of thinking." When we combine The Value Creation Strategy of Innovation, The Breakthrough Strategy of Execution, and integrate the critical element of thinking created by the Big Ideas, we are able to move from ordinary thinking to extraordinary thinking. Figure 34, duplicated below, shows the relationship of The Value Creation Strategy, The Breakthrough Strategy, and the twelve Big Ideas from ICRA. Value Creation, Breakthrough, and the Big Ideas combine to provide a thought system that is synonymous with Leadership.

		STRATEGY FOR BREAKTHROUGH PERFORMANCE			
		Identification	Characterization	Optimization	Validation
STRATEGY FOR VALUE CREATION	Innovation	Need	Value	Opportunity	Innovation
	Configuration	Idea	Determinism	Leverage	Configuration
	Realization	Measurement	Power	Transformation	Realization
	Attenuation	Uncertainty	Complexity	Risk	Attenuation

The Twelve Big Ideas from ICRA are shaded.

Figure 34 Relationship Between ICRA and ICOV

Each of the twelve Big Ideas in the above figure is rooted in specific phases of the ICRA and ICOV, i.e., Need is rooted in the Innovation phase of ICRA and the Identification phase of ICOV. However, it is important to recognize that the Big Ideas are critical elements that apply throughout the entire thought system from Innovation to Execution. In fact, we presented four additional Big

Ideas that were included in The Ten Supreme Laws and not ICRA: Vision, Position, Velocity, and Constancy. All sixteen Big Ideas apply to Mikel's complete thought system and every phase of ICRA and ICOV.

The thoughts relating the twelve Big Ideas rooted in the four phases of ICRA are well described in *The Six Sigma Fieldbook*. With permission, I have used this work in the concluding section of this chapter. I have reorganized much of the writing in the *Fieldbook* and added some of my original thoughts, but due to the number of direct quotations, have omitted the quotation marks, with permission, so as not to be distracting.

Inspiration (Innovation)

The three Big Ideas rooted in the Inspiration (Innovation) phase of ICRA are Need, Value, and Opportunity. Mikel expressed these three Big Ideas in equation form linked to what he called "Causative and Relational Ideas" that transform thinking for a particular Big Idea. In other words, these are the causative concepts we should consider when looking at a particular Big Idea.

$$\text{Need} = \text{Experience} - \text{Entitlement}$$

$$\text{Value} = \text{Utility} \times \text{Access} \times \text{Worth}$$

$$\text{Opportunity} = \text{Condition} \times \text{Advantage}$$

The equations Mikel developed are based on the concept that a Big Idea is a function of two or more Causative or Relational Ideas. When two or more Causative or Relational Ideas are adjusted, we can control the magnitude of the Big Idea. Paraphrasing Jack Welch, former CEO of General Electric, a Causative and Relational Ideas framework of thought allows us to get to the control function of reasoning.

The operators in the equations have specific meaning. If the operator is multiplicative, then it means that the Causative and Relational Ideas occur jointly, even though they are fully independent. If the operator is additive, then the Causative and Relational Ideas cannot occur jointly, as they are mutually exclusive. The Causative and Relational Ideas can either occur at the same time and place, or they cannot occur at the same time and place. We will not go into a detailed explanation relating all of the Big Ideas to their associated Causative and Relational Ideas but will provide enough examples to help you understand how the operators work.

The Causative and Relational Ideas associated with Need are Experience and Entitlement. While you must have both elements to create a need, the idea of Experience (observation) does not interact synergistically with the idea of entitlement (the standards or objectives that have been set). They play off each other in an additive, not multiplicative, way. We have an experience when we come into contact with a deliverable. We also have a rightful level of expectation (entitlement). The difference between the two is either positive, negative, or zero. The size of the negative result is synonymous with the size of the need. Any positive value represents the extent the need was exceeded. The main point is that the Causative and Relational Ideas associated with Need do not occur jointly.

Opportunity comprises the Causative and Relational Ideas of Condition and Advantage. Therefore, an opportunity is a set of conditions configured such that they have an advantage in achieving an envisioned end.

Configuration

The three Big Ideas rooted in the Configuration phase of ICRA are Idea, Determinism, and Leverage. Expressed in equation form:

$$\textbf{Idea} = \textbf{Reasoning x Context}$$

$$\textbf{Determinism} = \textbf{Element x Causation}$$

$$\textbf{Leverage} = \textbf{Force x Span x Advantage}$$

The two Causative and Relational Ideas associated with Idea are Reasoning and Context. Since we cannot reason outside a context, the two problematic ideas are multiplicative—they occur jointly. They interact with each other to generate an outcome or idea. Both reasoning and context must occur at the same time to successfully form an idea.

Leverage is defined as a function of Force, Span, and Advantage. Mikel interpreted Force as being the depth of knowledge delivered, i.e., Champions, Master Black Belts, Black Belts, Green Belts, Yellow Belts, and Span as being the number of people trained. From this perspective Force times Span was the amount of work (knowledge) delivered. This does not align with work as we would calculate from the physics perspective (Work = Force x Displacement x Cos Φ), but it works conceptually. By creating an advantage for delivering knowledge, we create Leverage.

Realization

The three Big Ideas rooted in the Realization phase of ICRA are Measurement, Power, and Transformation. Expressed in equation form:

$$\textbf{Measurement = Observation x Scale}$$

$$\textbf{Power = Force x Span} \div \textbf{Time}$$

$$\textbf{Transformation = Change x Induction}$$

Mikel defines the Big Idea of Power as being the composite of force, span, and time. As noted in our discussion on leverage, Mikel considered work conceptually to be Force times Span. Thus:

$$\textbf{Power = Work} \div \textbf{Time}$$

$$\textbf{Power = Force x Span} \div \textbf{Time}$$

By jointly considering the Big Ideas of Power and Leverage, we open a gateway of thinking driven by the Causative and Relational Ideas. By integrating these ideas, we are in a much better position to create value.

Attenuation

The three Big Ideas rooted in the Attenuation phase of ICRA are Uncertainty, Complexity, and Risk. Expressed in equation form:

$$\textbf{Uncertainty = Total} - \textbf{Probable}$$

$$\textbf{Complexity = Node + Connections}$$

$$\textbf{Risk = Loss x Exposure}$$

When a business sets out to create value in the interest of meeting a customer need, it introduces the risk of not meeting that need. The simple act of designing a process, product, or service creates as much risk as opportunity. Anytime we take an idea out of its potential realm (design) and transform that idea into its kinetic state (operations), we risk doing so without adhering to specifications. The idea of Risk is meaningless in the absence of exposure and loss. Anytime we marry capability with specifications, we create risk, or more accurately, exposure to risk. The portion of the distribution of outcomes falling outside the lower and upper specification limits is the area of exposure. However, this portion is not synonymous with the probability of risk or the probability of loss. Only when this possibility (exposure) is manifested in the form of a defect (nonconformance to standard), have we experienced an actual risk consequence or loss.

While there is risk in the stock market, for instance, we are not exposed to that risk if we are not invested in it. Therefore, we cannot experience loss. If we are invested, then we are exposed. But this does not mean that we will necessarily experience loss (although exposure always precedes loss).

Combining Big Ideas

We noted previously that it would be limiting to think that the Big Ideas only apply at a particular ICRA phase, i.e., Idea, Determinism, and Leverage; or that they only apply with respect to Innovation; or that Measurement, Power, and Transformation only apply to Realization. Big Ideas form a checklist of thought that we should consider at every phase of ICRA and every phase of The Breakthrough Strategy, whether it be ICOV (RDMAICSI) or The Great Discovery. ICRA is a prescriptive technique for Innovation, while ICOV and The Great Discovery are prescriptive techniques for Execution. Big Ideas are not prescriptive. Big Ideas form to make a checklist of concepts that we apply throughout the System of Thought developed by Mikel, a System of Thought that is synonymous with how leaders think: Leadership.

The *Fieldbook* shows how Big Ideas can interact or interrelate. For example, take the two Big Ideas of Idea and Power.

$$\text{Idea} = \text{Reasoning} \times \text{Context}$$

$$\text{Power} = \text{Force} \times \text{Span} \div \text{Time}$$

Mikel shows that by manipulating these ideas algebraically, Big Ideas combine philosophically to become deterministically operable. In this specific example, the interactions and interrelations from these concepts can be combined to form "Idea Power."

$$\text{Idea Power} = \frac{\text{Reasoning} \times \text{Context} \times \text{Force} \times \text{Span}}{\text{Time}}$$

Since the operators in the numerator are all multiplication, the concepts of Reasoning, Context, Force, and Span all must jointly occur to create Idea Power. Only by jointly changing Reasoning, Context, Force, Span, and Time in a positive way can we improve Idea Power.

The equation for Idea Power can be reduced to:

$$\text{Idea Power} = \frac{(\text{Reasoning Force}) \times (\text{Context Span})}{\text{Time}}$$

Looking at the equation in context of Mikel's interpretation—Force is depth of knowledge and Span is breath of knowledge—is consistent with Mikel's Six Sigma deployment philosophy:

- Train at all levels of knowledge, i.e., Champions, Master Black Belts, Black Belts, Green Belts, Yellow Belts.

- Do so with as many projects that you can support, providing Context Span.

- Do so in the shortest Time possible.

Combining these ideas is what will lead to a successful deployment. While this was Mikel's philosophy for deploying Six Sigma, it applies equally when engaging in the improvement of any issue.

By combining Reasoning and Force and Context and Span, we can see that we increase our Idea Power by either increasing our Reasoning Force or Context Span or by reducing Time. Mikel goes on to equate Reasoning Force with the idea of intellectual capability or IQ and Context Span with the idea of problem difficulty, noting the more difficult the problem, the higher the IQ, the greater the Idea Power.

$$\text{Idea Power} = \frac{\text{(Intellectual Capability) x (Problem Difficulty)}}{\text{Time}}$$

Mikel then combines Intellectual Capability and Problem Difficulty into one term: **Applied Intellectual Intelligence.**

$$\text{Idea Power} = \frac{\text{Applied Intellectual Intelligence}}{\text{Time}}$$

Mikel calls Applied Intellectual Intelligence per unit of time, Intellectual Productivity.

As you can see, understanding the Big Ideas is just a starting point for Leaders to develop their thinking. Mikel not only combined the Big Ideas but, as he combined them, went through an Innovative thought process searching for synonyms that allowed him to simplify the combined idea into a contextual form.

Let's look at another simplification of Idea Power:

$$\text{Idea Power} = \frac{\text{(Reasoning Span) x (Context Force)}}{\text{Time}}$$

Reasoning Span can be interpreted as Intellectual Capacity, and Context Force can be interpreted as Issue Priority. Time can be more specifically defined as Intervention Time resulting in the following:

$$\text{Idea Power} = \frac{\textbf{Knowledge Concentration}}{\textbf{Intervention Time}}$$

Idea Power = Issue Resolution Efficacy

Mikel called this type of thinking "Philomathic Thinking." Philomathic comes from two Greek words that together mean lover of learning. Mikel simplified Philomathic Thinking in the words in which we are more familiar:

> Key thoughts are identified, characterized, optimized, and validated. Then they are organized and rolled together to create a tsunami of reasoning—the mental equivalent of breakthrough. The Causative and Relational Ideas roll up into Big Ideas, which then roll together to fuel the strategic ideas in the Value Creation Strategy of ICRA and the Breakthrough Strategies of ICOV (RDMAICSI) and The Great Discovery.

Philomathic Thinking opens the portals and pathways of logical thought. One Big Idea links with another and melds into another, synonyms are substituted, leading to a near-infinite number of possible permutations. As such, Philomathic Thinking, in and of itself, teaches leaders how to be Innovative Thinkers and complex problem solvers. As Mikel notes, "even when only two Big Ideas overlap, they never overlap the same way twice. Each separate context, each nuance—no matter how simple or complex—makes each idea unique."

One of my peer reviewers focused on the idea that I was trying to convey Six Sigma as Leadership. No, what I am expressing is much more important. Mikel's thought processes show leaders how to think things through. Learning how to use all of these tools with facility will not happen overnight. Nonetheless, Mikel's Leadership Model is teachable and repeatable.

Mikel Harry's thought processes—which consist of the Breakthrough models of ICOV (RDMAICSI) and The Great Discovery, and combined with the Innovation model of ICRA, and when integrated with Big Ideas and Philomathic Thinking—are the way leaders should think.

In this way, Mikel Harry's thought processes serve as the very foundation of Leadership.

References

[1] Harry, Mikel J., *The Nature of Six Sigma Quality*, Motorola University Press, 1988

[2] Forever Missed, *Mikel J. Harry Ph.D.*, www.forevermissed.com/mikel-j-harry-ph-d/

[3] Marash, Stanley A., Paul Berman, and Michael Flynn, *Fusion Management: Harnessing the Power of Six Sigma, Lean, ISO 9001:2000, Malcolm Baldrige, TQM, and Other Quality Breakthroughs of the Past Century,* QSU Publishing, 2004.

[4] Harry, Mikel, and Don R. Linsenmann. *The Six Sigma Fieldbook: How DuPont Successfully Implemented the Six Sigma M;anagement Breakthrough Strategy.* Currency Doubleday, 2006.

[5] Montgomery, Douglas C. *Introduction to Statistical Quality Control,* 7th Edition. John Wiley and Sons, 2013.

[6] Capper, Richard. *A Project-by-Project Approach to Quality: A Practical Handbook for Individuals, Teams and Organizations.* Gower Publishing Limited, 1998.

[7] Schroeder, Alice. *The Snowball: Warren Buffet and the Business Life.* Bantam Books, 2008.

[8] McKeown, Greg. *Essentialism: The Disciplined Pursuit of Less.* Crown Business, 2014.

[9] Biehl, Bobb. www.bobbbiehl.com/

[10] Ingle, Sud. *In Search of Perfection: How to Create/Maintain/Improve Quality.* Prentice-Hall, 1985.

[11] Juran, Joseph M. *Managerial Breakthrough: A New Concept of the Manager's Job.* McGraw-Hill Book Company, 1964.

[12] Drucker, Peter F. *The Practice of Management.* Harper and Row Publishers, 1954.

[13] *Merriam-Webster Dictionary.*, 2018. www.merriam-webster.com

[14] *Roget's 21st Century Thesaurus.* Third Edition, The Philip Lief Group, 2013. www.Thesaurus.com

[15] Kruse, Kevin. "What is Leadership." www.forbes.com, April 9, 2013.

[16] Main, Jeremy. *Quality Wars: The Triumphs and Defeats of American Business.* A Juran Institute Report. The Free Press a division of Macmillan, Inc. 1994.

[17] Harry, Mikel, and Richard Schroeder. *Six Sigma: The Breakthrough Management Strategy Revolutionizing the World's Top Corporations.* Currency, 2000.

[18] Harry, Dr. Mikel J. www.sixsigmamindpro.com

[19] Eckes, George. *The Six Sigma Revolution: How General Electric and other Turned Process into Profits.* John Wiley & Sons, Inc., 2001.

[20] Harry, Mikel J., and Catherine Lawson. *The Great Discovery: A Process That Creates Breakthrough In Everything You Do.* The Great Discovery LLC, 2010.

[21] Trine, Ralph Waldo. *In Tune with the Infinite: Or, Fullness of Peace, Power, and Plenty.* Dodd, Mead, & Company, 1897.

[22] Vilhauer, Jennice PhD. "3 Effective Visualization Techniques to Change Your Life." *Psychology Today*, Sussex Publishers. www.psychologytoday.com.

[23] Kahneman, Daniel. *Thinking, Fast and Slow.* New York: Farrar, Straus and Giroux, 2011.

[24] Leduc, Alan M. *Passion in the Wind. Dream, Believe, and Achieve the Extraordinary.* Extraordinary Press, 2011.

[25] Galvin, Robert W. *The Idea of Ideas.* Motorola University Press, 1991.

[26] Osborn, Alex. *Your Creative Power: How To Use Imagination.* Charles Scribner's and Sons, 1948

[27] Baruch, Bernard M. *Baruch: My Own Story*, Henry Holt and Company, 1957

[28] *Google Dictionary.* 2019. www.google.com

[29] Keynes, John Maynard. *The General Theory of Employment, Interest and Money.* Palgrave Macmillan, 1936.

[30] Ishikawa, Kaoru. *Guide to Quality Control.* JUSE, 1968.

[31] Maslow, Abraham H. "A Theory of Human Motivation." Psychological Review, 50, 370-396, 1943 via www.psychclassics.yorku.ca/Maslow/motivation.htm, 2019.

[32] Lewin, Kurt, *Principles of Topological Psychology*, McGraw Hill Book Company, Inc.

[33] Senge, Peter M. *The Fifth Discipline: The Art & Practice of The Learning Organization.* Currency Doubleday, 1990.

[34] Knight, Frank H *Risk. Uncertainty and Profit.* Houghton Mifflin. 1921.

[35] Deming, W. Edwards. *Quality, Productivity, and Competitive Position.* Massachusetts Institute of Technology Center for Advanced Engineering Study, 1982.

[36] Deming, W. Edwards, *Out of Crisis.* Massachusetts Institute of Technology, 2000.

[37] Mol, Michael J. and Julian Birkinshaw. *Giant Steps in Management: Creating Innovations That change The Way We Work.* Pearson Education Limited, 2008.

Index

Made in the USA
Columbia, SC
06 January 2020

86163007R00117